SCIENCE
LOOKS AT
ITSELF

SCIENCE
LOOKS AT
ITSELF

COMPILED AND EDITED BY

National Science Teachers Association

NEW YORK • CHARLES SCRIBNER'S SONS

CONTENTS

PREFACE

THIS book came into being as a result of a series of programs called Silver Symposia sponsored by the National Science Teachers Association during two weekends in April 1969 as a part of the Association's observance of its twenty-fifth anniversary. Each of these programs consisted of a major session in which the general public was invited to join with science teachers in considering the insights that science can bring (or is, or is not, bringing) to bear on some of today's crucial areas of public concern. At more than one hundred such meetings across the nation, the public, science teachers, and eminent speakers from government, education, and science did indeed enter into such discussions. The result for all who participated was an enriched understanding of science's role in intellectual and cultural progress, of how it continues to develop in importance and interest to those who leave the classroom and school laboratory to become active participants in this age of science and technology. Our speakers provided insights into problems and described tools already at hand to be used. They pointed to past errors, warned of a future where the inexorable "laws" of nature are disregarded, and revealed the dimensions of the decisions that must inevitably follow new knowledge. The papers presented here offer a sample of their views.

That speakers of the caliber of the men represented in this book were willing to join with teachers and fellow citizens to explore these problems testifies to the seriousness of the problems and the validity of the views presented. The Association is indebted to all who helped to plan the programs or participated in them and is especially grateful to Charles Scribner's Sons for offering these discussions to a still wider audience of interested, concerned citizens.

NSTA is a nonprofit, nationwide society of teachers of science and others associated with, or interested in, science education. The Association is dedicated to the improvement and advancement of the teaching of science at all levels of instruction and to the improved preparation of science teachers. Through its publications program and its workshops and conferences, the Association serves its 22,000 members and the science teaching profession in such areas of concern as curriculum development and evaluation, coordination of the work of national and international organizations concerned with particular aspects of science and science teaching, and the delineation of special issues of concern to the profession. NSTA is an associated organization of the National Education Association and an affiliate of the American Association for the Advancement of Science.

The general organizing committee for the Silver Symposia programs on science and public problems was headed by Milton O. Pella of the University of Wisconsin. Other members were Alfred B. Butler, Washington State University; Serafino Giuliani, San Diego (California) Public Schools; Vern Gunderson, Prairie Du Chien (Wisconsin) High School; John J. Montean, University of Rochester (New York); John W. Renner, University of Oklahoma; H. Craig Sipe, State University of New York at Albany; John S. Richardson (deceased), The Ohio State University; and Elizabeth Simendinger Belasco, The Wheatley School, Old Westbury,

New York, president of NSTA, 1968-1969.

The papers were assembled and reviewed by Professor Pella, Mary E. Hawkins, Associate Executive Secretary of NSTA, and Sally L. Banks of the NSTA editorial staff, who was the editor for the papers selected for publication. For information about the various contributors see About The Authors at the end of the book.

ROBERT H. CARLETON
Executive Secretary
National Science Teachers Association

INTRODUCTION

THIS collection of essays, *Science Looks at Itself,* expresses the modern equivalent of the position taken by Thoreau in a book review which he wrote in 1843. The review, sarcastically entitled "Paradise (To Be) Regained," attacked with passion and wit the book *The Paradise within the Reach of all Men, without Labor, by Powers of Nature and Machinery,* in which J. A. Etzler had asserted that Paradise could be recreated on earth by technological innovations that would solve all human problems and eliminate the physical exertion from the world.

Thoreau naturally took a dim view of Etzler's quantitative mechanical utopianism. He scornfully labeled it "transcendentalism in mechanics" and "the utopia of the crank or push button," and questioned whether the machines devised by "Mr. Smooth It Away" could ever replace man in the most meaningful tasks of life. More importantly, Thoreau developed the view that the technological approach to environmental problems could never substitute for the ecological approach (although he did not use the word ecology, which had not then been invented). As was his wont, he expressed in a metaphor his sympathy for the ecological attitude toward society: "Can we do no more than cut and trim the forest? can we not assist in its interior economy, in the circulation of the sap?"

Since Thoreau's time, many humanists and social critics have expressed alarm over the consequences of industrialization for man's life and the environment. Until a few decades ago, however, scientists and technologists saw no reason for such concern, taking for granted that the products and procedures their activities yielded would inevitably prove useful to mankind. *Science Looks at Itself* is a timely and important book because it reflects a profound change in this euphoric attitude. Most scientists are now deeply concerned with the social implication of their work; they no longer believe that scientific and technological feasibility constitute sufficient criteria for decision and action.

No one questions, of course, that science and technology have contributed enormously to the welfare of mankind; their achievements have outstripped those anticipated by our eighteenth- and nineteenth-century ancestors. Even those of our contemporaries who are hostile to technology acknowledge the power of science. The revolutionary advances of the past two centuries and the promise of many more such advances to come warrant the conviction that almost any specific problem can be solved by the application of scientific knowledge.

Nevertheless, it is obvious that something has gone wrong during the past few decades. Increased control over nature is not providing safety and peace of mind; economic prosperity is not making people healthier or happier; technological innovations create problems of their own, which continually necessitate the development of new countertechnologies. The feeling prevails that scientists have not yet learned how to direct their attention to the distressing aspects of the modern world that have their origin in scientific technology. Many persons go so far as to believe that the natural sciences are doing more harm than good.

The role of scientific knowledge in modern life is indeed an ambiguous one. Nuclear science is an excellent symbol of the two faces of scientific enterprise: it promises endless sources of energy, but it also makes it possible to build ever more destructive weapons. While new discoveries and technological achievements have unquestionably resulted in a host of desirable effects, the cost for most of these is eventually exacted in the form of new maladjustments and of threats to the welfare of humanity and the environment.

To a very large extent, the dangers for which science and technology are held responsible derive in reality from the craving of modern societies for rapid and continued growth. If populations continue to increase beyond the capacity of the earth to support them adequately and to absorb their waste products, if modern man expands still further his apparently insatiable appetite for the creations of industry, then disasters are inevitable because scientific knowledge cannot possibly provide methods to cope with such human excesses.

In the final analysis, the future of civilization depends upon man's ability and willingness to formulate goals that are both desirable and attainable. This book indicates some of the ways science can help in this task. At present, all too often there exists a painful discrepancy between what man aims for and what he gets. He builds machines to escape from physical work, but becomes their slave and experiences boredom. (The social disturbances that are likely to result from automation are so apparent that they have begun to preoccupy social conscience even before they have occurred on a significant scale.)

The social body is threatened by dangers which are inherent in undisciplined technological growth. Society already suffers from the problems posed by crowding, air pollution, automobile traffic, and by countless products of industrial life. Since so little effort has been made to control the effects of social and technological innovations on human life, man gives the impression that he is practicing—not by intention but by inaction—a kind of biological warfare against nature, against himself, and, especially, against his descendants. In fact, the pages of newspapers and magazines bear witness to the public's somber anticipation that the legend of the sorcerer's apprentice may soon be converted from a literary symbol into a terrifying reality.

Biology and anthropology teach us that many species and societies have died as a result of overdeveloping the very specializations and achievements that had been responsible for their success in the early phase of their evolution. Many great civilizations of the past became so intoxicated with their social or technological proficiency that they collapsed under the weight of their own creations —as symbolized by the fate of Gothic architecture.

The architects of the late Gothic style had such confidence in their skill that they built higher and higher structures with more and more flamboyant ogives; and, as a result, the high towers collapsed, as in Beauvais, leaving only immense soulless bodies. It does not take much imagination to see in these architectural castrophies a symbol of what might be in store for our civilization.

The very efficiency of our technological civilization may contribute to its undoing. Through specialization in knowledge, in management, and in technical skills, our society has succeeded in producing an extraordinary state of adaptedness between human life and the environment it creates. But this adaptedness and the efficiency which it makes possible impose severe limitations on the freedom to change. These limitations imply a fundamental conservatism which substitutes endless play with trivial details for significantly progressive changes.

The history of living things shows that, in general, the biological species which are most specialized and efficient find it difficult to undergo adaptive modifications when placed in a new environment, and there are indications that, for human societies as well, adaptability decreases with increasing specialization. An overspecialized and overadapted culture like that of the United States might find it difficult, for example, to move on to the next phase of human evolution, to get over the divide which separates present-day industrial civilization from a more sophisticated social and cultural way of life.

The contributors to this book point to many of the dangers inherent in our civilization. One general aspect of their message may provide the formula through which scientific technology can be maintained as the servant of man instead of being allowed to become his master.

Even though the power of science and technology will continue to increase, industrial societies cannot continue much longer to produce more and more of everything, for larger and larger numbers of people. The following factors, and many others, will soon compel a reorientation of the scientific and technological enterprise.

(1) World population will stop growing and may even decrease—hopefully through deliberate control of birthrates but more probably as a result of biological disasters.

(2) The amount of power used for industrial and domestic purposes will eventually reach a plateau, not because of a shortage of energy sources, but because the injection of excessive amounts of energy into natural systems inevitably leads to ecological disturbances.

(3) The quantity of things produced by technology will also reach a plateau, because of shortages in certain natural resources and because environmental pollution will reach unbearable levels. We cannot delay much longer the development of a nearly "closed" system in which materials will retain their value throughout the system by being recycled instead of discarded.

Many persons mistakenly assume that constraints on population and technological growth will lead the world into a period of stagnation and, eventually, of decadence. But I believe that a closed system is compatible with a continuous process of creative changes, and that changes within a closed system will offer intellectual challenges far more interesting than those associated with the kind of rampant economic growth that has characterized the nineteenth and twentieth centuries. We cannot have a scientific and technological renaissance, however, until we develop new conceptual ideas about design on a grand scale. A science of social design will certainly emerge if we abandon quantitative growth as a value for its own sake, and learn instead to use ecological constraints as creative stimuli for the management of human life on the spaceship Earth.

Thoreau symbolized this ecological view of modern society in the metaphor quoted earlier. For scientists, technologists, and sociologists, the metaphor means that the most important problem today is not so much to produce more goods and services, but to regulate the interplay between man and his environment. Unfortunately, successful regulation is much more difficult to accomplish than increased production. A new kind of knowledge is needed to maintain the multiple components of the complex man-environment system in a viable form.

Science, according to Sir Peter Medawar, is "the art of the soluble." But this felicitous phrase does not throw light on the relative social importance of the various problems that are soluble. For the socially oriented scientist, to know what ought to be done is as essential as to know what can be solved. In any case, there is no doubt that social constraints will increasingly influence the direction of the scientific enterprise, for the simple reason that the public is now aware of the deep effects of science on all aspects of life.

The execution of any complex program demands specialized knowledge and must therefore be delegated to experts. Likewise, the prediction of the probable consequences of a given course of action is the province of experts. But the role of the educated general public is just as meaningful as that of experts in any program of social importance because in the formulation of plans, goals are in the long run more significant than means.

This does not mean that everyone should become a scientist. But it demands that the citizen acquire the kind of awareness that helps him recognize and evaluate the cultural and social consequences of scientific technology. By contributing to this awareness, *Science Looks at Itself* will help us to escape the tyranny of the expert, who should not be allowed to become decision maker without being responsible to the community.

RENÉ DUBOS
Member and Professor
The Rockefeller University

SCIENCE
LOOKS AT
ITSELF

Purpose, Property, and Environmental Disaster

ROY A. RAPPAPORT

One of the most pressing of the technology-based problems confronting modern man is the despoiling of the natural environment—a process which began when man became an ecological dominant through the institution of agriculture. This process, vastly increasing in tempo in the twentieth century, now poses a threat to the very existence of the species *Homo sapiens*. Dr. Rappaport suggests that natural scientists—and, by projection, all whose lives are affected by the advance of the natural sciences—can learn a vital and humbling lesson from the study of the relationship of nonindustrial man to his environment.

ONE of the premises of anthropology is that, whatever else he may be, man is an animal. As such, he is bound indissolubly to his environment. He has the same needs as other animals, and his populations are limited by similar factors. The notion that man has freed himself from environmental limitations through the conquest of nature is not simply a misunderstanding or an analytic error. It is something much more dangerous, for it leads to actions which must in the long run be disastrous. The attitude engendered by this belief is reminiscent of what the Greeks called *hubris,* an arrogance so great that it led men to challenge the gods and led the gods to respond by destroying them.

Man has not conquered nature, although he has debauched her. And lately she has been warning man that she is preparing to punish him. For instance, atmospheric pollution resulting from industrial and automotive combustion is already producing a "greenhouse effect" which can result in a significant rise in the earth's temperature. An increase of 5 or 6 degrees would be sufficient to melt the polar ice caps and would result in a rise in sea level of some hundreds of feet, inundating many coastal areas.

The British-American anthropologist Gregory Bateson has suggested that one factor responsible for such ecological problems lies in the very nature of human consciousness. Man is accustomed, if not actually genetically

programmed, to think in terms of goals. To accomplish goal
C, one takes actions, *A*, then *B*. The pattern is linear (action
A, action B, goal C), and, moreover, the goals are likely
to be narrowly defined in terms of immediate self-interest.
But the world is not constructed in such linear fashion.
Ecosystems are more or less circular in plan. Materials of
vegetable origin are cycled through herbivores, carnivores,
decomposers, the soil, and back into plants. These cycles
are very complex, and only recently have they begun to be
understood. But it is clear that if one component of the
system is affected, all are likely to be affected. Man's
goal-directed behavior, then, affects not only one component of his environment, which we called *C,* but many
other components as well, not to mention man himself.[1]
Thus, in the pursuit of self-interested goals, men, through
ignorance, arrogance, or greed, almost invariably violate the
ecosystems outside of which they themselves cannot
survive.

Bateson's suggestion is a gloomy one, for goal-directed
thinking has contributed greatly to man's survival during
most of his 3 million years on earth. During most of this
time man, like other animals, subsisted on the products of
hunting and gathering. His purposefulness—which, combined with his other mental powers (imagination, foresight,
and so on), made man an extremely successful animal—
was no more dangerous to the ecosystems in which he
participated than was the purposefulness which surely
must form a component of the consciousness of lions,
elephants, and other animals.

6   But here let me note a lesson, not only of anthropology,

but of biological evolution and, if history has any lessons at all, of history too. Species and societies die of that which made them flourish. The very specializations that at one time have contributed to the survival of many species have led eventually to their extinction. And so it is with civilizations: Rome's organization demanded and made possible the conquest of more lands than she could administer when conditions changed markedly.

Man's purposefulness, which has been highly adaptive under certain circumstances, may eventually lead to his downfall. The trouble apparently began about ten millennia ago, for it was about then that men began to cultivate foodstuffs. In cultivating, man becomes an ecological dominant, the species which sets the conditions that encourage or discourage the presence of other species in an ecosystem. To cultivate, man replaces stable and mature associations of plants and animals (known as climax communities) with associations of his own devising. Man-dominated ecosystems, anthropocentric ecosystems, are composed of species selected by man for inclusion according to criteria of his own self-interest and are arranged by him into a limited number of short food chains for all of which man himself is supposed to be the terminus.

Anthropocentric communities are likely to be both less stable and less productive than were the climax communities they replace—and are likely to include fewer species. The relatively degraded nature of these anthropocentric communities is in part a function of their simplicity, in part a function of their constituents. As a rule of thumb, the more species present in a community, the greater its

7

productivity (that is, the greater amount of living tissue produced per unit area per unit time). Moreover, the species present in the climax community are present because they are adapted to their surroundings. In contrast, many of the species included in anthropocentric communities are exotics, introduced by man merely because they yield materials useful to him, and only poorly adapted to the habitats into which they have been introduced. These exotic species need constant protection. Many cannot even reproduce themselves very well without human intervention.

So anthropocentric communities—cultivated communities—are in an absolute sense, degraded in comparison with natural climax communities. Man's advances have been won at the expense of introducing instability into the systems in which he participates. Moreover, he has taken upon himself the burden of maintaining equilibrium in the unstable systems which he has devised. Far from freeing man from his environment, the assumption of the role of ecological dominant has made man the slave of his own living invention.

Man makes a poor dominant. It is interesting to observe that in nonanthropocentric ecosystems of any extent the dominants are always, or almost always, plants. Oak trees dominate some temperate forests; algae dominate reef-lagoon ecosystems. Plants, because they are nonpurposeful, are well suited to be dominants: Their mere existence fulfills the role, and the conditions which they set for other species therefore tend to be stable. Men, on the other hand, must act to maintain their dominance, and action is less reliable than mere existence. Furthermore, men are capable of making mistakes, and their goals are not always compatible with the requirements of the systems which they dominate. For these reasons, and because even the best laid plans of men are often disrupted, the conditions which they set are unstable.

I am not suggesting that we go back to hunting and gathering. Indeed, while it was the development of plant and animal culture and the assumption of ecological dominance that may have first introduced instability into the ecosystems in which man has participated, primitive agriculturalists were—and in a few isolated pockets here and there in the world continue to be—rather successful in maintaining equilibria in their ecosystems.

It is civilized man, particularly recent civilized man, who has really disrupted his environment. In large measure this has been caused by his increased ability to alter his world—a lot more damage can be done with a bulldozer than with a digging stick. But technology is, after all, an outcome of knowledge, and increased knowledge has not been an unmixed blessing. It has produced a technology that not only augments man's ability to alter, but augments it at a much faster rate than it increases his ability to regulate—that is, to maintain equilibria in the systems which he dominates. Knowledge has become increasingly —wittingly or unwittingly—the handmaiden of environmental destruction.

It is natural that ability to alter has advanced faster than ability to regulate. For one thing, the intellectual processes associated with alteration are much simpler than are those associated with regulation. To alter, one needs simply to formulate goals and to understand something of the gross properties of the equipment and materials to be manipulated in achieving them. Little detailed knowledge of the structure of the universe is required. In contrast, successful regulation—that is, keeping the components of a structure in some sort of viable balance—requires sensitivity to the less obvious aspects of systems structure. When alteration is considered, the important questions to be asked about, say, a tree, might be: How much time will it take to cut it down? What bearing characteristics will timbers fashioned from it have? Such questions are obvious, and they are easy to answer because they are concerned with a few specific characteristics of a limited number of objects. The universe of inquiry in such an instance is limited. Regulation, on the other hand, would require questions about the relationship of the tree to other plants and animals and to such soil components as nitrogen. Such questions are not obvious, and even when they are raised, they are hard to answer because the universe of inquiry is extremely large. Their answers are likely to be complex for the same reason. And even if such inquiries were to yield considerable knowledge of the systems in which men participate, this knowledge might be self-defeating.

The primitive horticulturist, who knows less about his ecosystem than we know of ours—he probably has no idea of the existence of trace elements in the soil, for instance—at least *respects* the processes whose operations he does not understand. Although he does not know of what his ecosystem is composed, he is sensitive to the limits within which he can operate. Frequently components of his ecosystem are associated with the supernatural, and among the New Guinea people with whom I have worked, religious beliefs and practices actually focus upon ecosystem regulation.[2] With increased knowledge, however, comes the attitude that ecological processes are natural, not supernatural, and can be manipulated. And so they can, to some extent. But a little knowledge is notoriously dangerous; to tamper with ecosystemic regulation is to tamper with the operation of a system whose full workings are not now understood and, because of their complexity, are likely never to be understood completely.

This does not mean that man should not attempt the regulation as well as the alteration of ecosystems, but such behavior must be predicated on the assumption that he is participating in systems that he does not fully comprehend. Respect must compensate for lack of knowledge. As Bateson has also noted, the religions of primitive peoples—often predicated upon a respect for ecosystems which the worshipers do not understand—are more far-seeing than those of the Judeo-Christian tradition, which propound the absurd notion that everything on earth was created for man's enjoyment or use.

As the situation now exists, man can alter that which he cannot yet regulate, and may never be able to regulate, and the rate of alteration accelerates with no end in sight. How did this situation develop? It has surely been a likely outcome of the growth of industry and the vast organizations which operate industry. In the United States these

11

organizations remain largely in the "private sector" of the economy, and, in my view, private enterprise has made a particularly terrible contribution to the present state of the environment. Because private enterprise in all its vitality and diversity was instrumental in the development of our country, Americans have sanctified enterprise and allowed it to continue to direct development. But when "development" means achievement of the self-interest goals of private industrial organizations and when it employs our increasingly powerful technology to do so, it becomes a euphemism for environmental destruction.[3] As often as not it accomplishes the short-term benefit of the few but results in the long-term and not-so-long-term deprivation of the many of their right to an environment unpolluted by smog and industrial waste, an environment in which at least some redwoods survive. To correct the famous remark of former Secretary of Defense Charles E. Wilson, what is good for General Motors is not necessarily good for the United States, much less for the natural world of which the United States is only a part.

A related notion which exists almost unquestioned is the right of individuals to use lands to which they have title in almost any way they choose. Such ideas of property rights are very rare among the world's societies. In most non-Western societies, a man's rights in his own land are limited; he is not permitted to use it in ways which are detrimental to the society at large. When one thinks about it, it is absurd that anyone who by a mere act of purchase has come into temporary possession of a piece of land that has been in existence since the beginning of time should be allowed to use it as he will except for very minor restrictions.

I am not advocating the abolition of private property or of private development. But I *am* arguing that, in addition to bringing industry, which has developed purposes of its own, back into the service of living things, our society must invent much more effective means of regulating the use of private property and the activities of private developers and must do everything possible to put such regulating mechanisms into effect. This will not be easy. Not only are powerful interests opposed; their opposition is supported by industry's past successes and is sanctified by some of America's most cherished beliefs. But the lesson of history, of anthropology, of evolution, remains clear: Populations, nations, whole species have been destroyed by that which made them great.

Must
Economic
Expansion
Doom
the Environment?

CHARLES H. STODDARD

How can the seemingly inexorable process of environmental destruction be stopped? Private enterprise must be indicted for much of the degradation of our natural resources. Now it is the responsibility of private enterprise, and the federal government as well, to take immediate and concrete action to restore the viability of man's environment. Mr. Stoddard outlines some of the steps which can, and must, be taken in this sphere.

DURING the past two centuries, efforts of Western man to solve economic problems have met with extraordinary success. By developing new technologies, employing them in huge urban-industrial complexes, and inventing social organizations for their management, the Western world has achieved vast industrial outputs. Poverty has been reduced and living standards have been raised. Since World War II the gross national product of the United States has more than doubled. But at what cost?

An expanding population requires ever more space for homes, businesses, and service facilities of all kinds. Coal is stripped from mountainsides to provide for rising electrical energy needs; thousand-year-old redwoods are felled to supply such "essentials" as patio furniture; and pesticides strewn about fields and forests to increase food and wood-fiber production prove lethal to both fish and bird populations. All the outdoors is a disposal system for the nation's wastes.

The lessons of the interrelationship between man and his surroundings have been written large in damage to the waters and landscape of twentieth-century America. Few have read these lessons, however, and even fewer read them with understanding. Forecasters of economic growth foresee even greater acceleration of America's overheated industrial system during the next thirty years, an acceleration which will bring with it increased consumption of natural resources and production of effluent by-products to pollute the environment.

17

A basic clash between further economic growth and the capability of the environment either to absorb or to support wastes seems inevitable. The major sources of air and water pollution are receiving some attention; so must the sources of land pollution, which include the improper disposal of solid wastes, unplanned urban expansion, and damage to scenic and natural values.

How do we go about improving our technology so as to meet more desirable environmental goals? Upon analysis, seven points emerge:

(1) It is clear that unless present unplanned development and waste disposal are curtailed, the environment is headed for even more rapid deterioration.

(2) It is equally clear that long-overdue water pollution treatment facilities—both industrial and municipal—must be installed immediately to arrest this deterioration. (Nationwide, the backlog of investment in needed waste facilities has increased from $6 billion to $26 billion in ten years—despite major efforts during the 1960s.)

(3) It may be less clear that, even if this backlog is disposed of, the real threat in the foreseeable future is the acceleration of our economic growth and population expansion, the effluent of which could bring on final disaster.

(4) It has become essential to think about the plan for built-in prevention of pollution, as well as for correction of existing pollution sources, if present trends are to be reversed. This means the acceleration of technology of waste *utilization,* not simply treatment.

18

(5) Only recently has discussion begun about "recy-

cling" as a means of prevention. Prevention can and should consist of recycling presently wasted materials by considering them a natural resource to be utilized, not something to be thrown away. Fertilizers, minerals, useful chemicals, and other by-products needed by our economy can be derived from currently wasted resources. (The pioneering work of the Milwaukee Sanitary Commission produced commercial organic fertilizer at a loss but turned loose fewer solids and produced some revenue.)

(6) Subsidizing the cost of utilizing these waste materials is an intelligent alternative to spending large sums to treat them only partially and then disposing of their residual effluents to pollute air and water.

(7) And finally, it is imperative that special and immediate attention be given to control of three new types of pollution—nuclear, thermal, and agricultural pesticides —which, if left unattended, could undo all of our present efforts to control other sources.

The important fact is that there *are* alternatives. There are choices which can and must be made in the management of natural resources and environment. Neither environmental decay in the form of a slow, unobtrusive decline in the quality of our surroundings nor environmental destruction through a nuclear accident should be an inevitable result of industrial progress.

Choosing between available alternatives will require the development of intelligent, long-range public policies on environmental quality and on the administration of the environment. While some significant progress toward this end has already been made, the movement of

19

government from the role of arbiter among conflicting resource interests to that of trustee for the environment as a whole is still far from complete.

For too long government has merely reacted to environmental crises rather than anticipating and avoiding them. The future will require that more effort be spent on treating the causes, rather than the symptoms, of environmental decay.

In the past, most governmental action to ensure environmental quality has proceeded on a case-by-case problem-solving basis. When the need for the preservation of natural values was felt, a system of national parks was established; when widespread erosion threatened the landscape, the Soil Conservation Service was established; when water- and air-pollution problems proved to be more than the state governments alone could handle, federal programs were established; and so on. Reacting to particular crises case by case is not sufficient if we are to preserve and maintain environment quality. There are far too many cases. An effective program of environmental administration will require adjustments in the existing structure of our government.

But governmental responsibility alone will not be enough. There must also be private responsibility for environmental quality—individual and corporate self-discipline. The issue: how to build in environmental safeguards early in the decision-making process.

What practical alternatives do we have if we are to meet the challenge which economic growth poses to our environment? Will we simply generate more conflict, with

20

conservationists fighting rearguard actions which they lose more often than not? Must we slow down or halt economic growth? Or can we manage it, channel it, guide it by requiring economic decisions that take into account social costs and environmental damage?

The first requisite for a responsible program of environmental management is a planning body in the executive branch of the federal government. This is not a new idea. There have been legislative proposals in recent years to establish a Council of Environmental Quality Advisors in the Office of the President, with proposed supervision, assessment, policy recommendations, and veto power over construction of highways and dams, use of pesticides, urban redevelopment, and the thousand and one other developmental actions of the federal government. In early 1970 a federal Council on Environmental Quality was, in fact, established by law. Earlier, President Nixon had formed a cabinet-level Committee on the Environment, and a parallel Citizens Advisory Committee was also appointed. Similar groups were appointed under the Johnson administration, but despite three years of operation, the effectiveness of all these groups is still to be determined.

Consolidation of the federal government's natural-resources functions into one department to assure consistency of policy and coordination of programs is a second proposal, one which was suggested by the first Hoover Commission and also recommended by the Acheson-Pollock-Rowe Task Force in 1949. Many of the states have already adopted this pattern for comparable functions.

21 A third essential element is a strong, capably staffed,

and adequately financed citizens' political-action organization for environmental conservation. Such a group would exert pressure on decision makers of federal and state agencies and private corporate organizations and would counterbalance the special-interest pressures which now usually prevail.

What reasonable demands might such groups make? With existing technology the decision makers for any new development project that would cause environmental disturbance could be required to make provision in the basic design for recovery of waste and avoidance of landscape damage, thus reducing environmental deterioration to a minimum. For example, if highways and electrical transmission or telephone lines were built along existing corridors, the despoiling of the remaining landscape would be avoided. Setback and cluster designs could be used to preserve open space in new subdivisions and along lakes and rivers. Buildings should not be erected on flood plains, which could be used for parks or other public facilities.

Strip mining should be outlawed on mountainsides. Backfilling, grading, and revegetation should be required after mining on more level lands.

All new municipal developments and industrial or utility plants should be required to construct complete waste-recovery units (cooling towers for nuclear power plants, recycling ponds for paper mills and taconite plants, and so forth) so as to avoid the need for later cleanups. And, finally, it is senseless to build those facilities which we know in advance will add to pollution or environmental deterioration: supersonic transports with their air pollution and noise, nuclear plants with accidental waste potential, dams and roads in reserved wilderness areas, and airports and freeways around wildlife areas.

At present, sanitary engineers, landscape designers, regional planners, foresters, and ecologists are rarely called in at the design stage by the single-purpose decision makers. The reasons are probably fear of increased costs and unwillingness to broaden narrow objectives and consider factors other than engineering and economic efficiency. Decision makers must come to realize that:

(1) Any and all economic growth may not be good *per se*.

(2) The economics of efficiency should not be the sole criterion by which to judge decisions affecting the environment.

(3) Criteria must be broadened to include noneconomic environmental factors.

Here I throw out a challenge to the economists. They have been lax in investigating the economics of waste, and especially the economics of environmental damage. It is safe to predict that the able economist who makes this fertile field his specialty will soon catapult into the national limelight. Preliminary data have shown that proper design and installation of waste-recovery equipment adds less than 5 percent to the unit cost of most manufactured products. There is every reason to believe that the cost to society of the damage caused by pollution will exceed the cost of abatement. But the cost of pollution is borne by the public, while the high profits from low-cost manufacturing processes accrue to the polluter alone. Human society should be at least equally concerned with the qualitative—as opposed to the material—aspects of economic development as it affects the environment and conditions of life. Doesn't an economy which litters its landscape with old automobiles, an unused source of raw material, and simultaneously processes taconite ore in such a manner as to pollute Lake Superior, the last clear lake of the Great Lakes system, deserve an agonizing reappraisal?

Professor Arnold Reitze of Case–Western Reserve School of Law suggests that pollution abatement facilities should be treated as a business expense for immediate write-off for those concerns already causing environmental damage.[1] All new plants should include abatement and amelioration facilities in the basic cost of the original design. Reitze further suggests that an effluent tax should be placed on all polluters, as is done in the Ruhr Valley, where taxation and fines act as a successful deterrent to pollution.

Our experience in establishing laws and administrative agencies to deal with pollution has been almost dismal. I know of no lake or river in the United States which has been polluted and is now cleaned up. Faced with political pressure and interference from polluters, and the ensuing bureaucratic indecision, we are daily losing ground.

The major hope for safeguarding the habitability of the earth is to modify the current technological linkages between industrial activity and environmental pollution. The essential task of society is to develop a pollution-free technology, both in order to maintain the viability of already industrialized nations and to ensure that the vast surge of

24

industrial activity will include a technology which will not corrupt the earth with mass pollution. Requiring the recycling of waste and considering it as a new source of raw material would make short shrift of effluent pollutants.

Sooner, rather than later, we must be able to prove Joseph Wood Krutch to have been in error when he said, "There is increasing evidence that man's ingenuity outruns his intelligence. And that though competent to run a primitive world, man may not be competent to manage the more complicated and closely integrated world which he is, for the time, powerful enough to destroy."[2] Our main hope is a much tougher approach than we have taken to date. As the Red Queen said to Alice in *Through the Looking Glass*, "It takes all the running you can do, to keep in the same place. If you want to get somewhere else, you must run at least twice as fast as that."

Using
the Power
of
Prediction

JOHN H. HELLER

So often the solutions to one problem only create new and unforeseen dilemmas. Dr. Heller argues that, before rushing to embrace any new technological panacea, society must pause to weigh the predictions which can be made about its possible outcomes. Scientists do have the ability to make valid predictions about problems of environmental quality, population control, or public health. It must be the role of government and private research organizations to support such prediction, and of the citizenry to demand it.

Scientists have the ability to make predictions, on the basis of what they know and on the basis of what has gone before. But the social instrumentalities that tend to control science seem reluctant to admit that this inherent predictivity exists. Government—and sometimes industry—is not taking a positive position and moving forward to meet situations. It reacts rather than acts.

The possible result of an experiment should be considered before the experiment is conducted. For example, many scientists agree that within the Milky Way Galaxy there are at least a hundred thousand planets that may support sentient life. There have been and still are extensive programs studying radio phenomena from space. One of these, Project Ozma, conducted at the Green Bank Observatory in Green Bank, West Virginia, in 1960 sought to detect intelligent signals from elsewhere in the universe. Suppose that such a program should sometime prove successful. Suppose a voice from, say, Alpha Centauri replies to our signals. What will be the reaction—delighted cries of "We are not alone!" or a global panic?

The subject of insecticides may seem more mundane. In fact, there probably is no living creature on the face of the earth that does not contain some DDT or similar substance in its body. The long-range effects of many of these substances are not known as yet. This is the kind of situation that should be anticipated by corporations and

government and society as a whole before major research

efforts are undertaken. Alternatives do exist—for example, in the case of insecticides. Better techniques are available. Insect hormones can be purified, identified, and synthesized and used as a spray, which apparently has an effect on no other living thing but which can cause a weird and disproportionate development on the part of the insect, making him incapable of moving—hence he starves to death. (Almost the ultimate in insecticides, one might say.) When the chemical research that underlies modern insecticides was being done, twenty to forty years ago, scientists had the option to go one way or the other. The decision was made, and now there is an insecticide problem.

At the time the first antibiotic substances—the sulfonamide drugs, the prontosils—were developed, in the early 1930s, any small group of scientists could have projected with a high degree of accuracy that a population explosion was inescapable. It was known then, and it is still true today, that the largest factor in population control is infant and neonatal mortality, and the greatest effect of the antibiotic drugs is to reduce this mortality. The time to plan for this expanding population in terms of increased housing and food production and methods of population control was *then,* not now when the situation has reached crisis proportions.

This kind of predictivity continues to be available, and failure to exercise it will affect the future as it has the past.

Hundreds of millions of dollars are spent in the United States and in other advanced countries throughout the world for research on cancer and cardiovascular disease.

Within a reasonable time, advances will be made in the cure of both of these diseases. When this happens, there will be an escalation of longevity of about eight to fourteen years. This will not halt the aging process: people are going to be just as senile, have just as many broken hips, more strokes, and more paralysis. The life span will be extended, but, highly predictably, the problem of caring for the aged will be tremendously expanded.

The least that society could do—the very least—is to create more geriatric homes and train more people to take care of the aged. But even that is not being done. On the other hand, the most effective action would be to retard the rate of senescence. Scientists think this may be possible, but there are virtually no research dollars in the United States for this kind of work. The type of research thus far supported in geriatrics or gerontology has concerned the treatment of the symptoms of aging. Science should be pursuing something more basic, something which would make it reasonable to predict a significant retardation of aging.

An example of such a project involves DNA, the master genetic-controlling molecule. There are various laws in science which suggest that everything runs down eventually. For instance, in the case of the master steel disk which punches out records, after the millionth or two-millionth or five-millionth record is made, there is a decrease in fidelity, and there will be blurring and scratching. The working of the steel disk is analogous to the working of DNA as it continually replicates itself to make new structures, new cells, to replace those structures that are aged or injured. What happens, in so far as data now show, is that it gets blurred; it gets scratchy; it runs down. Those structures that are replaced, then, as a function of injury and time do not have the same fidelity as do young tissues.

Suppose, therefore, that a scientist were to take a sample of a man's blood, culture the white blood cells, and harvest the DNA. The DNA would not deteriorate if it were kept at liquid-helium temperature. As senescence of mind and body began to occur, the DNA could be injected back into the man's cells, diluting the aged DNA with more juvenile DNA. What would happen? The answer is not yet known, but it is hoped that such a technique could retard the *rate* of senescence. Scientists do not anticipate that man will live longer than his preprogrammed genetic age dictates, be it three-score years and ten or four score and ten— every species has a preprogrammed genetic age—but they believe that man will have the possibility of staying younger in mind and body throughout senescence.

Scientific prediction points to a future problem. The least society can do in the face of this prediction is to provide a haven for the aged, the senile, the paralyzed; the best that it can do is to try to do something definitive to retard the aging process. There is very little serious activity to produce the first solution; there is very little activity of any kind to produce the second. Yet research in cancer and cardiovascular disease has been going on for decades, and its success will drastically increase the population of the upper age brackets.

A related area of worldwide concern is overpopulation. Even a problem of such overwhelming magnitude as this can profit from the efficient application of what is now known and what can be predicted. Current publications abound with dire statistics of overcrowding in many parts of the world, but less omnipresent are the data concerning the converse of that problem. France, a nominally Catholic country, has maintained a virtually stable population since the time of Napoleon. What are the French doing wrong—or right—that is not known about or understood? The Soviet Union is another example. The USSR scientific community apparently agrees—only the timetable is in dispute—that in three hundred or five hundred years there will be no Russians left. The birth rate is declining so disastrously at the present that it is merely a matter of time until there will be no more Soviets. It is possible to deduce some factors which help to explain these situations in France and Russia, and it seems rather puzzling that demographers and other concerned professionals who have not been able to succeed in reducing the high birth rates in places such as Latin America and India have not investigated biological and sociological causes of the opposite phenomena in two very large nations and have not attempted to extrapolate them where the situation is most acute.

Predictivity is the factor which could put man in a singularly useful position to cope with the future, but he is not now using this predictivity to any serious social or political extent. Man merely lets things happen: pollution happens; overpopulation happens; new diseases which are a function of our social and technological progress happen. Society is not using the kind of predictivity which it might

33

in an intelligent way in order to provide a better future for mankind.

What are the possibilities for scientific action in social problems? Consider the following phenomenon: If a biologist is shown a large number of animals of the same species and asked if, after he has studied enough of them for a sufficient period of time, he will be able to tell something about them, the answer will be "Absolutely yes," and he *can*. Now man is an animal; he exists in abundant supply (billions) and has been extant for thousands of years. Has anyone said anything definitive about man? People ranging from philosophers to economists to social scientists to historians all have hypotheses and theses concerning the animal, man, but they can neither prove them nor disprove them because they cannot quantify or mathematize them. Therefore people can construct hypotheses endlessly and no one can truly gainsay anyone else, although some do shout a little louder than others.

I want to suggest that the natural scientists *can* look at the societal phenomena of man and his actions and reactions. Instinct, for example, might be considered a genetic constraint of behavior which, in a particular environment, has a survival value for the species. If instinct is so regarded, then examination of such instinctual behavior as territoriality, herd instinct, protection of females and young, and self-preservation suggests that in all societal animals—from the ant, whose evolution stopped a long time ago, to man—there seem to be the same basic constraints of behavior. Such reactions as "Fifty-four forty or fight!" or "My home is my castle" are obvious manifestations of territoriality in our own culture. Any possibility of comparing one group of men with another is completely abrogated unless it can be established that both groups are really saying the same thing but that each has a different cultural way of affirming it.

It is also possible to weight these various instincts. For instance, a baboon is frightened to death of a leopard and will run from its spoor; but, if the leopard threatens baboon pups and females, the male baboons will subdue self-preservation—one instinct—and attack to protect the females and the young—another instinct. The baboons may be killed, but so will be the leopard. What exists in such a case is a weight relationship of one instinct vis-à-vis another. Elaboration on this kind of relationship would allow the mathematizing of some factors of human behavior.

Can this kind of study be used to shed light on the problems in our cities? Or, even more important, to shed light on the bellicosity among peoples which leads to war?

It is impossible to know until the attempt is made; and, when and if it is made, it must involve the scientific community, the private sector, government, and society as a whole in the planning—not just for the scientific endeavor itself, but for its possible and predictable consequences. Among those things which *can* be predicted is this: If man does not undertake this four-way dialogue soon, if he does not use his inherent predictivity, he will be inviting the whirlwinds of disaster.

The Risks
of
Disbelief

WALTER L. SAUNDERS

Implicit in the crises discussed in the preceding articles is society's failure to believe in and accept the data available to us. Man continues to live as though such threats—already documented and made public—simply do not exist. Dr. Saunders examines the power of disbelief and concomitant factors which lull us into comfortable complacency in the face of the awesome potentials of our age.

We are living in an age which future historians may well describe as a very primitive period of transition. Man continues to cling to cherished beliefs, many of which have served him well in the past, and is unwilling to concede that some of these beliefs have lost their validity in the world which exists today. It has become man's custom to look to technology for solutions to so many of today's problems that many people fail to realize that even technology has its limitations; that there are problems for which there are no technical solutions.[1] Many of these problems—war, destruction of the environment, the population explosion—have in fact been inflated as a result of technological advances.

Man must accept the need for human solutions, and he must accept the often painful adjustments that such solutions entail. Some privileges long taken for granted may now be privileges that the human race cannot afford. Attitudes which were once merely unrealistic reflections of what man wanted to believe may now prove disastrous. Thus, some implications for the teaching of science become very clear. It is essential to instill in today's students a belief in the process of science as a way of dealing with the real world, as a valid way of connecting cause and effect, and as a reliable basis for gathering decision-making data. They must understand that technology alone cannot solve our most serious problems; it is a tool of man and must be intelligently controlled and directed by man.

Barry Commoner, in *Science and Survival*, has eloquently presented a number of cases in which scientific capabilities, like the sorcerer's apprentice, have created situations far more dangerous than were the situations they were developed to deal with.[2] Let us examine two such cases, both dealt with by Commoner, which suggest that man's unwillingness to believe in the potentially destructive power of science and technology to destroy human and environmental values is an operative factor in allowing such threats to man's existence to continue.

In 1960, Norbert Wiener, the father of the science of cybernetics, in reviewing a decade of progress in science, reported on the development of a computer that had been programmed to play checkers.[3] Built into the system of electronic circuits in this new kind of automatic machine was an understanding of the rules of checkers and, in addition, a way of determining what kinds of moves were most likely to defeat the computer's opponent. An additional capability of the circuitry was the ability to record the moves of the opponent in his present and previous checker games. The opponent's most likely moves in any given situation could be calculated at great speed, allowing the computer to judge its own most profitable move at any given time. Thus, in effect, the engineers had designed an electronic machine that not only knew how to play checkers but, like a human player, could learn from its past experience and actually improve its own game. In describing the results of early checker tournaments between computers and their programmers, Dr. Wiener notes that the machine started out by playing an accurate but uninspired game and frequently lost. After some hours of practice, however, the computer got the hang of the game, and from then on, the human player usually lost. Man had succeeded, Dr. Wiener concluded, in building an automatic machine that escaped from his complete, effective control.

Now, clearly, a checker-playing machine capable of defeating the very man who designed and programmed it does not, in and of itself, constitute a threat to man. But the nature of the relationship between man and the machine he has made has rather disturbing implications. What is the quality in man's own nature that motivates him to apply his intelligence to the creation of something which has the capacity to surpass his intelligence? What are the implications for the future?

Let us now consider a second case from Commoner, a somewhat different—and terrifyingly serious—illustration of a problem with no technical solution based on a 1963 Rand Corporation report on civilian defense analysis.

"To kill 60 percent of the United States population (about 120,000,000 people): 500 10-megaton bombs dropped on centers of industry.

"To destroy 100 percent of the port capacity of the United States: 40 10-megaton bombs (400 megatons total) dropped on ports.

"To destroy 100 percent of petroleum refinery capacity of the United States: 150 10-megaton bombs dropped on petroleum refineries.

"To destroy 90 percent of United States heavy industry: 300 10-megaton bombs (3,000 megatons total) dropped on centers of such industry.

41 "To burn out about 10,000 square miles of vegetation:

1 10-megaton bomb. Under very "favorable" conditions in a forest area a single 1-megaton bomb would burn out about 8,000 square miles.

"To burn all vegetation on 50 percent of the United States land area: an attack with a total of about 7,500 megatons of weapons. (Estimates are extremely variable; the area that would be burned out in a 1,500-megaton attack has been estimated at from 5 to 80 percent of the total United States area.)

"To destroy by fallout radiation the usefulness of 91 percent of United States cropland and to destroy 95 percent of hog production, 94 percent of milk production, and 88 percent of all cattle: an attack totaling 23,000 megatons on combined military and population targets.

"To destroy the usefulness of 44 percent of United States cropland and to destroy 55 percent of hog production, 68 percent of milk production, and 46 percent of all cattle: an attack totaling 9,000 megatons on combined military and population targets.

"Taking into account these effects (which assume that bombs are delivered to different targets with complete accuracy), the probable inaccuracy of missiles (which is rather small), and the different possible patterns of attack, we can arrive at a general estimate of the over-all destruction. An attack of 5,000 to 10,000 megations would not immediately "wipe out" the nation; some people (about 30 percent) and some food-producing capacity (something less than 50 percent) would remain."[4]

But these figures do not tell the whole story. A major nuclear attack would drastically reduce the size and composition of the surviving population. The Rand Corporation notes that, due to the uneven geographical distribution of people engaged in various occupations, a 2,000-megaton attack would kill 73 percent of the nation's architects, 69 percent of the chemists, 62 percent of the physicians, 72 to 86 percent of various kinds of engineers, 64 percent of all machinists, and 76 percent of all tool and die makers. Other factors complicate the probability of survival in a nuclear attack.

The advent of a nuclear attack would most probably severely decrease the effectiveness of public health programs, resulting in large-scale secondary effects due to spreading of disease at epidemic rates.

Commoner concludes that a society which survived a nuclear attack would be poised precariously between recovery and further deterioration. Failure to begin the process of recovery very soon after the attack would probably lead to rapid degeneration. For example, competition for food might lead to inefficient use of the foodstuffs available, which would impair recovery efforts. Shortages would grow more severe; conflict would increase; "the social system would start on a descending spiral toward disintegration."[5]

Couple these data and predictions on the probable effects of a nuclear attack with recent newspaper reports concerning the overkill capability of the United States' arsenal (and of our enemies' arsenals) for chemical and biological warfare and one is forced to conclude that for the first time in the history of this planet a species of living organisms has acquired the capacity to render itself, and possibly all other life forms, extinct.

43   While the above data are known to be quite reliable,

the actions of the United States, and of other nations as well, reflect disbelief: witness the current Vietnam "peace-keeping" effort. Man now has the technological capacity to carry military conflict to its extreme—total annihilation. Nevertheless, military conflict continues to take place on a limited scale, indicating an incredible optimism in man which allows him to believe that the scale can be kept "limited" and providing concrete evidence that he has not relinquished the belief that war is an acceptable means of resolving conflict and that he refuses to accept the predictions of the Rand report and others like it.

Yet the ultimate solution to conflict must come from within man. There is no technical solution. The development of more powerful and more terrifying weapons will not solve the problem, it will only escalate it.

The destruction of the environment constitutes a second threat to man's survival. An examination of the "green-house effect" will clarify man's continuing role in the alteration of the atmosphere.

For a long time fire has been a crucial tool in man's survival. Early man made use of fire to keep warm, to frighten away dangerous animals, and to cook food. Later man learned to harness the energy of fire to do his work with such devices as the steam engines and crude internal combustion engines. Today man has been able to devise the sophisticated steam-driven hydroelectric plant, as well as the complex internal combustion engine in our modern automobile and the reliable jet engine in our air-craft. Certainly a major force which has contributed to the development of modern-day heat engines is economic

44

gain. Private enterprise has played a most important role in stimulating more efficient use of resources and knowledge.

But let us examine the burning process. Modern man burns wood, coal, and all manner of petroleum products, including natural gas. Man burns iron ore in order to obtain iron with which to manufacture internal combustion engines, which burn petroleum products. Man burns a crude oil product, natural gas, in order to refine crude oil to obtain gasoline, which is burned in internal combustion engines. Thus man burns the materials of the earth to manufacture machines which, in turn, burn more materials and do man's work. Furthermore, man finds it necessary to burn in order to destroy his worn-out products. He burns garbage to dispose of it. He burns gasoline or diesel oil in order to burn garbage. He must burn in order to melt old automobiles. And burning adds carbon dioxide to the atmosphere.

Carbon dioxide plays an important role in regulating the temperature of the earth because while it tends to transmit visible light, it absorbs infrared energy which is converted to heat (the greenhouse effect). An increase in the carbon dioxide content of the atmosphere will therefore result in an overall increase of the earth's surface temperature. Between 1860 and 1960, the combustion of fuels added nearly 14 percent to the carbon dioxide content of the air. (Prior to 1860, the carbon dioxide content of the air had remained constant for many centuries.)

A report by the President's Science Advisory Committee contains a most discomforting prediction.[6] The extra heat

45

resulting from the fuel-produced carbon dioxide accumulating in the air may, by the year 2000, be sufficient to melt the Antarctic ice cap. There is enough water held in the Antarctic ice cap to raise the world sea level by 400 feet. Clearly this would result in a catastrophe for large portions of the earth's inhabited land.

And so man is again confronted with a problem which has no technical solution. He can measure the increase in the carbon dioxide in his atmosphere; he knows the consequences of that increase. At the same time he finds that he has made a tremendous economic investment in the manufacture of carbon-dioxide-producing heat engines and believes he must continue the manufacture of those heat engines. Clearly, the competitive structure of our economic enterprise is a significant factor in this dilemma. (A second factor involved in the relationship between science and economics arises out of man's attempt to maximize individual welfare at the expense of group welfare.)

The American biologist Garrett Hardin, in his article entitled "The Tragedy of the Commons," illustrates this aspect with a simplified version of the cattle grazing problem.[7] Since each herdsman seeks to maximize his own economic gain, he must always ask, "What is the utility of adding one more animal to my herd?" Each herdsman will receive all of the proceeds from the sale of his one additional animal, and, therefore, the positive value of adding one more animal to his herd becomes almost +1. The negative value of adding one more animal to the herd, however, is simply related to the degree of overgrazing that would result. But since the effect of overgrazing is spread amongst all of the herdsmen who use the common grazing land, the negative value of adding one animal turns out to be a fraction of the positive value. Since the net positive value of adding one more animal to his herd will always be $1 - 1/n$, where $n =$ the number of herds, and as long as n is greater than 1—that is, as long as there are at least two herds grazing the same land—the herdsman will decide that it is sensible to add an additional animal to his herd. He believes that this can be his only decision, since it is always to his personal gain to add an animal. However, since this is the case for all herdsmen in the herd, the herdsmen seem to be locked into a system which tends to bring ruin to all. Each one is pursuing his own best interest in a society that believes in freedom of common grazing ground, and the very nature of the system results in overgrazing which eventually affects all.

A second instance of Hardin's "commons tragedy" is the problem of water pollution. A man who owns a factory on the edge of a river finds that the disadvantage of releasing wastes into the river is less for him individually than is the cost (monetary) of purifying his waste before releasing it into the river. The true cost of the businessman's act is divided among all the people who use the river, be it for food, for recreation, or for aesthetic satisfactions. And the cost to these people can only partially be reckoned in dollars and cents.

Once again man is shown to be the victim of his own inventiveness. His intelligence has created a scientific-economic system which threatens his future existence and even now impairs the quality of that existence. If man's freedom to use his environment however he chooses continues, then he has won the continuing right to foul his own nest.

A third crucial problem facing man today is the population explosion. The price of the solution to this problem is the sacrifice of another of man's cherished privileges— the right to have as many children as he wishes. A recent declaration of the United Nations defends that right:

"The universal declaration of human rights describes the family as the natural and fundamental unit of society. It follows that choice and decision with regard to the size of the family must irrevocably rest with the family itself and cannot be made by anyone else."[8]

Most people would prefer to accept that statement unquestioningly, as we always have in the past. Yet as rational and objective human beings, we know that this ground rule cannot be a workable solution to the population explosion problem. A simple appeal to the good conscience of persons to limit the size of their families will not serve; the factors which now determine family size are too complex to be affected by such a naïve request.

The present rate of world population increase is known, and it is possible to predict the future rate of increase quite precisely, presuming no unforeseen crises occur. The surface of the earth is finite, the energy received from sunlight is finite, and the total food-producing capacity of the earth is finite. The only possible conclusion, therefore, is that there is a finite limit to the number of persons who can be sustained on the surface of this planet. But man
48 continues to live as though he does not believe these facts.

The technical solutions to the problem of population control are useless if man refuses to acknowledge the pressing need to make wide use of them.

Human problems require human solutions. Man must acknowledge and overcome his disbelief in the validity of scientific prediction. He must alter an economic structure which enhances individual gain at the expense of the group. And, finally, he must overcome his feeling of impotence, his feeling that nothing he can do as an individual will make a difference in the problems which confront him because they are of such overwhelming magnitude. He must believe, and he must teach young people to believe, that one *can* have an effect.

I have drawn heavily from published materials partly to demonstrate that there are thoughtful and meaningful reports being made public constantly. We must study such reports and heed their lessons. Clearly, if the species called man is to continue to survive on the surface of this earth, he must confront his progeny with the true nature of the problems that threaten him. The answer to man's problems lies within man himself—he cannot look to a remote technology to provide magical solutions.

Who
Shall
Decide?

LEROY AUGENSTEIN

Technology may provide the answers to some of today's public problems but it is clear that others require the intervention of human ideals. Dr. Augenstein examines the complexities of human responsibility in an age when technological breakthroughs have vastly increased man's capability to save or destroy life. The arena of medicine, in which rapid strides have been made in such new techniques as transplants and genetic counseling, offers poignant examples of the necessity of assigning and accepting responsibility on a personal, compassionate level.

Today's science necessitates involvement in the ethical and moral problems which follow in its wake. Such problems must be acknowledged, and met in order to provide a framework in which to put our technologies to use. All too often it is assumed that any new finding turned up in the laboratory is automatically put to good use. Nothing could be farther from the truth. Unfortunately, almost every new science capability carries with it a very large price tag, and the price is responsibility—responsibility for some very difficult decisions. Equally unfortunately, society has not yet created a proper apparatus—whether at the federal, the local, or the individual level—to cope with the enormous complexities of the decisions which now must be made.

Science-related decision making at the federal level is beset with awesome problems. Some of the most difficult of these decisions occur in the process through which new drugs come onto the market. Here a federal agency, the Food and Drug Administration, has some authority at two points—at the proposed initiation of clinical testing on humans and at approval for interstate marketing of a new drug. Take the case, for example, of whether one should initiate tests on humans of certain drugs that have been found very effective in combating leukemia in laboratory animals. However, at least in animals, these drugs produce their effect by causing mix-ups in the chromosomes; and these mix-ups occur not only in the cancer cells but also in many of the

53

healthy, normal cells. As a result, a very worrisome fraction of the animals which are cured of leukemia suffer extremely severe side effects. Some 5 to 10 percent are either crippled or blinded or have convulsions or seizures. Furthermore, and perhaps of greatest concern, many of these serious mutations are passed on to the next generation. There is no clinical evidence that this happens in humans. However, if these drugs are tested on women of fifty-five or older, who are almost certainly not going to have any more children, it is their choice as to whether they want to save their own lives and take a chance with side effects. But certainly if the drugs are licensed for testing on women of forty or under, or on men of any age up to fifty or sixty, the problem is quite different.

Some people maintain—and I think it is self-evident—that most of the decisions on these drugs will not depend on scientific facts. They depend upon a very serious ethical question. One might contend, therefore, that an official buried six or seven layers deep in federal bureaucracy should not make this kind of decision. It can be argued that this official's function, and the function of people like him, should be merely to transmit information about the capabilities and the problems of these drugs and to leave the actual decision to the local level. Who there would decide?

In one group of decision makers at the local level are the doctors. To ask them to shoulder this kind of serious ethical responsibility is to add still another weight to an already staggering burden.

54   Or the individuals involved may wish to make the

decisions themselves. For example, I know that if a member of my family needed to be treated for leukemia, and there were any such drug on the market, I would bring pressure to bear on the doctors I know to get the drug, regardless of their own positions on the question. Here, then, is another proposal for decision making: Do not force the doctors to make the decisions; let them relay information about the capabilities and problems of a drug to the individuals involved and let them decide. But what if those individuals are children? If my own child were involved, my wife and I would save that child's life. We would not worry about the grandchildren at that point— we would worry about their welfare much, much later.

A scientist I know argues that doctors should always save a child's life when possible, and that, when the child gets to a knowledgeable age, he can be told of the possible hereditary effects of the drugs he has been given and can then decide what to do. So if I save the life of my little boy, who is now four years old, when he gets to be thirteen I will have to tell him, "Now that you have entered puberty and can potentially begin to procreate children, you present quite a hazard to the next generation. You should consider having yourself sterilized." Is that a realistic question to raise with a thirteen-year-old child?

I have suggested three levels at which decisions could be made. The first is the federal level, the Food and Drug Administration in this case. Decision making at this level removes the responsibility to someone who is quite remote from the outcome of his decision and immune to most pressure. The second alternative is the local level,

55

here the doctor, and the third is the individual. Where do *you* think the responsibility should lie?

One aspect of decision making at the local level is dramatically illustrated by the problem stemming from the shortage of kidney machines, machines so named because they are able to assume the vital functions normally performed by healthy kidneys. Such machines are so expensive that not every community has one, a situation which is expected to prevail for quite some time unless an unexpected and remarkable breakthrough is made. In most communities which do have a kidney machine, the number of applications from people who need the machine is five to thirty times greater than the number of patients which it can serve. This means that someone, somehow, must decide which people are to use the machine. Those who do not have access to it will die. The decision maker must live with the knowledge that he has signed a death certificate for every applicant whom he rejects, leaving only the day and hour blank.

To whom should such an awesome decision be entrusted? In most hospitals it is made by the doctors on the staff; in a few, by doctors and hospital administrators; and in a very few, by a panel of citizens.

I talked recently with a man and a woman from one of these panels. A block of machine time had become available, but there were eleven people who needed that one block of time. After much soul-searching, the panel narrowed these down to three. The first was a man of sixty-two, a noted author. He had a fine family of children and grandchildren. He was a prime candidate for the machine

56

because he was currently writing a novel depicting the forces at work on a youngster in the ghetto. The panel read the first three chapters in draft form, and they felt that if he could sustain the high quality of those chapters, if he could reach the level of excellence of his previous best seller, the completed book would be of tremendous social benefit. The panel could keep this man alive for the two years it would take him to finish his novel. If they chose him for the machine time, they would be voting to benefit society.

The second candidate was a middle-aged woman with three teen-aged daughters, an alcoholic trying to take the cure for the third time. If the panel chose her, they would be giving her a chance to retrieve a wholesome life and look after her daughters.

The third of this trio was a young man in his thirties. He was manager of a local loan company and had been very active in the community; in fact, he had been voted outstanding man of the year a few years before. But he had just deserted his family, possibly, the panel thought, to avoid becoming a burden to them.

This is the information that the panel had—about the same amount of information that any such panel has when it is asked to make a decision. What would *your* choice have been? the author? the mother? the younger man? Or have you declined to vote? Few individuals are in any way prepared to take on a task which involves the assignment of relative value to human beings in order to decide who will live and who will die.

57   Even if an apparatus for making such decisions can be

established at the federal or local levels, or both, there will still be situations when individuals like you and me, with the same, inevitable subjectivity, must make a life-and-death decision.

Decision making at the individual level may well be the most agonizing and difficult. Consider the following illustration. Each year I am asked to give a fair amount of genetic counseling, usually to couples who have either had, or have reason to suspect that they may give birth to, an abnormal child. The majority of these queries can be answered by looking up the trait in question and finding out whether or not it is a hereditary trait that can be passed on within the family. There are usually ten to twenty queries a year which are more difficult and which require a fair amount of close counseling with the people involved. Most of these cases come out very well because giving people information on which to base their decisions is usually of considerable value to them.

Occasionally, however, a case arises which raises many questions about who bears the responsibility for making serious ethical and moral decisions and at what point such decisions must be made. I became involved in a case like this when a couple expecting their fifth child came to consult me. One of their children, a mongoloid, had died before his first birthday; two of their children were normal; the fourth child, another mongoloid, was still alive. The couple wanted to know what the chances were that their unborn child would also be mongoloid. It was possible to give the parents fairly accurate information, because it is known that mongoloids have one whole extra chromosome—the tiniest of human chromosomes. In the majority of cases, this extra chromosome exists free in the cell, and the probability of its occurring is determined almost exclusively by tests on the mother. Given this mother's age and background, her chances for having another mongoloid should have been somewhere between one out of thirty-five and one out of forty. But, since the couple had already had two mongoloid children out of four, it appeared that this was not the common form of mongolism. It seemed probable that their two abnormal children exhibited the much rarer form in which the extra chromosome is attached to one of the longer, medium-sized chromosomes. If this was the case, the mother's chance for a repeat was not one out of thirty-five or forty, but one out of three. Blood cells from the living mongoloid child were examined, and it was found that he did exhibit the rarer, "piggy-back" type of mongolism.

This meant that this couple's chances for having another mongoloid were one out of three, but the chances were *two* out of three that the child would be normal. The parents wanted to know for sure. Arrangements were made, therefore, for their doctor to employ a fairly new kind of testing procedure in which a hypodermic needle is used to remove some fluid from the embryonic sac (the water sac that eventually occupies a fair amount of the womb); this test is made midway in the fourth month of pregnancy. The fluid thus obtained from the mother was sent to a laboratory where technicians stained the chromosomes and counted them. Ten days later I heard what I had hoped not to hear: The child had forty-seven, not forty-

59

six, chromosomes and was going to be the couple's third mongoloid.

The doctor who had originally referred the couple to me and had made arrangements for the tests now refused to tell the couple the results of the tests.

You probably feel that the doctor had an obligation to tell the family the results. Normally I would agree that he had, but in this case the doctor and the couple were the best of friends. The parents were Congregationalists, the doctor a conservative Catholic. I believe he hesitated to inform the parents because he feared that they would, on the basis of their long-standing friendship, bring great pressure to bear on him to perform an abortion—an act to which he was firmly opposed—or at least to make arrangements for one.

The couple's minister and I argued with the doctor at some length on the point of informing the parents of the test result, but by the seventh month of pregnancy, the parents still did not know that the child would be mongoloid. Whether or not an abortion should have been performed was purely academic at this point. The minister and I decided that since the parents should be given time to prepare themselves, we would go over the doctor's head. We made arrangements for a conference, but when I arrived for the meeting the mother had already been taken to the maternity ward.

The situation in the waiting room was perhaps the most explosive I have ever encountered. The father had been told the test results only fifteen minutes earlier. The mother was not only in labor, but in very abnormal labor, which if allowed to proceed another forty to fifty minutes would result in the death of the fetus. However, the fetus could be removed with no real danger to the mother, and an immediate cesarean could save both lives. "What's your advice on this?" I was asked when I entered the room. Let me ask you the same question: would you answer, "Do an immediate cesarean and save both lives"? Or would you say, "Wait until the fetal heartbeat stops"?

Did you decide you couldn't make a choice? I am sorry, but that is a luxury you do not have in a case like this. There is no such thing as a nonvote: indecision *is* a vote in this situation.

At this point we were told that the fetal heartbeat was sinking much more rapidly than was expected. The doctor turned to the father and said, "All right, John, you don't have forty minutes—you have exactly three minutes to make up your mind. Time is running out. What are you going to do?" And John stood there, shifting from foot to foot, arguing out loud with himself, unable to come to a decision. The doctor, after two or three minutes, abruptly spun on his heel and said, "If you can't make up your mind, I'm going to do what my conscience tells me." He left the room to perform a cesarean.

In the silence that followed, I spoke to the husband. "Look," I said. "You've still got to make a rather important decision. If, at the end of the operation, you show your wife the child, or even tell her it is mongoloid, the chances are very great that she will not be able to stand the psychological shock." I went on to describe two

61 somewhat comparable situations in which a sympathetic

judge had been willing to issue a substitute birth certificate which led the mother to believe that the child had been stillborn when in reality the child had been put into an institution, and the real birth certificate sealed in the judge's archives. Later, when the mother had passed the postpartum depression, a decision could be made as to whether or not she could stand the shock of knowing the truth. I strongly recommended following this course because it would assure maximum flexibility for later decisions. Both the doctor and the minister agreed.

We thought the father was going to accept this solution, but he suddenly changed his mind. He pounded the table and insisted, "I will not be responsible for making this decision alone. My wife and I have made tough decisions together before. I'll tell her, and we'll see where we're going from here."

Six hours after the operation, this very distraught father was allowed to see his wife and immediately told her about the child. She went into severe hysterics which were temporarily calmed by sedation. But a few days later she was found trying to kill the child. She is now irretrievably insane and constant observation is necessary to keep her from trying to rip off her breasts or otherwise defeminize herself.

Initially I condemned the father for his inability to accept individual responsibility for the two crucial decisions regarding the cesarean and the substitute birth certificate. But now I realize that he was not a weak man: he was simply a man unprepared and overwhelmed. I have also damned the doctor. But, in all fairness, had his beliefs, his background, his position been mine, I am not sure I would have done differently. I have also condemned the minister and myself for not taking more forceful action, although, having been in the case by invitation, we can wash our hands—in public. What deserves to be condemned is a system in which absolutely no one had clearcut responsibility when those critical decisions had to be made.

Hindsight is supposed to be better than foresight. Having heard the case, with whom would you place the responsibility for the ultimate tragedy? Should responsibility have rested with the individuals? For instance, the couple might have decided after the birth of their second mongoloid child to have no more children; the father, during the crucial hours in the waiting room, had two chances to accept the responsibility for making a decision, although he was given almost no time in which to make it. His unwillingness to decide alone may have cost his wife her sanity. Or should the doctor be held responsible? If he had informed the parents of the test results, much later agony might have been spared them. Or ought society to be blamed, represented in this case by the minister and me?

I cannot see any completely satisfactory solution to this case. Probably most people would prefer that individuals make as many decisions in this area as possible. And yet, one must be careful. I believe that the individual has the right—and the obligation—to determine his own destiny. But when I look at people in mental institutions, I realize that there is a line beyond which one dare not push people.

Shall we play God? I hope it is evident by now that we no longer have a choice. Once an individual is asked to make a decision like any of those faced during the progress of this case, no matter what he decides, he is playing God. If he decides on an immediate cesarean, for example, he risks the life of the mother. If he decides against the cesarean, he takes the life of the fetus. The real question is not "Shall we play God?" but rather "Who plays God, and what values does he bring to bear on his decisions?"

Science gives man capabilities. It does not instruct him in the use of those capabilities. But certainly any society is derelict in its duties if it does not call into clear focus the value judgments that must be made as science is put to use.

Certainly two and a half minutes is not enough time to make a vital decision unless one has examined his moral principles very closely before he faces the crisis. I have scrutinized my own values again and again since I have become involved in genetic counseling, and I have formulated some fundamental values which are essential if I am to function properly. (There is a clear distinction between fundamental values and operating procedures. Some people will say that, since the old operating procedures are no longer valid, everything is relative. I think that is incorrect. Granted that many of the old operating procedures are not working, and much of the old dogma is no longer valid. But that does not mean that the fundamental principles should be discarded; it just means they need to be reinterpreted.

64   One of my fundamental values is belief in an orderli-

ness underlying the workings of the universe. Wherever I look—whether it is in the atom, the gene, or the mind —I find this order. I, therefore, believe that there is an orderliness in the way you and I should behave toward each other. This implies that there is a right and a wrong. It does not imply that I can always exactly identify right and wrong, but it says that I have an obligation to seek them out. (Incidentally, this belief in orderliness is necessary to a research scientist. If there were no order, there would be no point in doing experiments, because one could not get a reliable answer.)

Another of my values is belief in the sanctity of life. Too many people are content with a very superficial definition of what life is. The recent advances in organ transplants have created an awareness of the complexities of the biological aspect of life. In the counseling situations in which I am involved, I have to consider at least three aspects of life: not only the biological, on which man has concentrated in the past, but also the psychological and the social. I believe in the sanctity of all three. Morality—that is, the exercise of values—must take into account these three aspects of life.

Suppose, for example, that on a given night three couples each conceive a child. The first couple is not married; they do not intend to marry; and they never see each other again after this night. The mother insists on keeping the child with her in the small town in which she lives, and both mother and child are ostracized. The second couple is married, but they know that they are passing on a set of defective genes to their unborn child. The child never knows who he is, and spends a life of suffering in an institution. The third couple is married and has good genes. However, they do not give their child a workable set of values, and he becomes a criminal. Which couple is most immoral? The first couple violated the social well-being of their child by submitting him to ridicule and ostracism. The second couple violated the biological sanctity of their child's life by giving him a bad set of genes. The third couple neglected the psychological aspect of their child's life.

In counseling, in decision making, all three life aspects must be considered. In some cases of genetic counseling, for example, I recommend abortion although, until a few years ago, I believed myself to be irrevocably opposed to it. Abortion violates the biological sanctity of the life of the unborn child, but to do otherwise in many cases is to do an even greater injustice to the psychological and/or social welfare of the child and others concerned.

Finally, the most important value or principle that should govern man's behavior toward his fellow man is the Greco-Christian concept of *agape*—nonpassionate, nonselfish love, man's obligation to be his brother's keeper. Some may have asked why I interfered in the lives of the couple who gave birth to a third mongoloid child. The reason is very simple—they asked me. Once they had asked, I had an obligation to try to help, even though there is some question as to whether I did more harm than good. For me to have refused would have been passing to the other side of the road.

66   Life is increasingly complicated, and new capabilities

produce new and more complicated ethical dilemmas. Though new laws and new apparatus for their application are essential, no judge or lawyer or legislator can ever write a law that will tell each individual what to do in each and every situation that may arise. No theologian can ever again write a set of dogmatic operating procedures that will cover each and every situation. The values of an individual will or will not be represented in the solution of contemporary problems to the extent that he is or is not willing to become personally involved and to commit himself in public. To Edmund Burke's famous injunction, "The only thing necessary for the triumph of evil is for good men to do nothing," I would add "to do nothing *in time*." And since the accelerated pace of scientific advance provides more and more capabilities—and more and more problems—every day, the time is very short.

The Way
of
Science

GALE W. McGEE

Society is often tempted to place the blame for many of the more frightening problems of today squarely at the feet of science, perhaps because to so many people science seems very remote and virtually incomprehensible. Senator McGee points out that technology has merely magnified society's weaknesses because society has failed to direct it properly. It is within the power of education to increase scientific literacy and to permit our young people to apply the dispassionate and exacting method of science to the problems which they find so disturbing.

The most profoundly significant aspects of science and technology in contemporary life are the speed with which they have brought about radical changes and the vast scope of those changes.

Leland Haworth, former Director of the National Science Foundation, writes, "In the span of less than a single lifetime, virtually every aspect of our society and our personal lives has been vitally affected by the tremendous impact of science and technology."[1] Such terms as "television," "jet," "lunar module," "nuclear power," and "cybernetics" were unknown just thirty years ago. And many a man on the sunny side of old age, watching on television as our astronauts explore the moon, can remember the first electric light.

Without this sudden impact and the bounty it bestows in the fields of medical science and nutrition, many people now alive would never have been born. The population of the world would still be less than a billion, rather than the present 3⅓ billion.

Many who have observed this impact and have watched as the products of technology have altered what once was, have worked to bring into accord the wizard products of research and development and the needs of the people in a democratic society. But it must be remembered that 1970's undergraduates were born and have grown up during an era just following the most radical of the changes all about us. To them, this is nothing new. It's like the "given" in a geometry problem.

It is important that these undergraduates understand that the last two decades were not just a happening. Those years represent a dramatic culmination; a time when a corner of the jigsaw puzzle began to fit together as undiscovered pieces were found. Do today's students believe, for example, that Albert Einstein "discovered" nuclear energy? The German-born physicist (1879-1955) would have been the first to deny it. The fact is, of course, that this most significant of all scientific findings was made possible by a host of researchers from many nations, each of whom advanced man's knowledge a few arduous steps up a very long ladder.

The climb began with the French chemist Antoine Laurent Lavoisier (1743-1794), and the list of those who continued it includes physicists Wilhelm Konrad Roentgen (1845-1923), a German; Antoine Henri Becquerel (1852-1908), a Frenchman; and Sir Joseph John Thomson (1856-1940), an Englishman. The French chemist Pierre Curie (1859-1906) and his Polish-born wife Marie (1867-1934), a physical chemist, made important additions, as did the British physicist Ernest Rutherford (1871-1937) and the Danish theoretical physicist Niels David Bohr (1885-1962). Enrico Fermi (1901-1954), the Italian-born American atomic and nuclear physicist; J. Robert Oppenheimer (1904-1967), the American theoretical physicist; and Sir James Chadwick, the British physicist, contributed their research. Each of these scientists, and many others in man's history, have contributed to the opulence technology now offers.

Science and technology are more than just the margin between linsey-woolsey and Orlon, between springhouse and deep freeze, between buggy whip and synchromesh; they have become an ever more dominant way of understanding the world. Unfortunately, the proportion of the population acquainted with the central propositions of contemporary science does not increase. The fact is that since 1900 there has been a tenfold increase—from 4 to 40 percent—in the proportion of the population of the United States which attends college. But understanding of the nature of science, the profoundest influence upon American society, has not increased on the same order.

I think some of this lack of understanding is apparent in the anger which is erupting at many colleges and universities. People tend to fear what they do not understand, and it is not really surprising that some young people should react vigorously against a society conditioned by a technology which sometimes seems to have its own random ends and purposes—or ends and purposes of which they disapprove.

Perhaps education of a somewhat different order would help resolve this problem. Though education ought not to be regarded as a panacea, certainly recourse to education is within our tradition, for our history shows countless Americans—indeed a whole nation—whose talents and resources have been increased in geometric progression by it. I am intrigued by an education proposal made by René Dubos. He writes: "The time has come when we must produce, alongside specialists, another class of scholars and citizens who have broad familiarity with the facts, methods and objectives of science and are thus capable of making judgments about scientific policies.[2]

The fact that mass can be converted into energy and

73

that matter can be destroyed by a human act, states James Bryant Conant, former president of Harvard University, in *Modern Science and Modern Man,* changes the whole nature of the universe.[3] This basic change is responsible also for the most awesome and important factor in the life of every man, woman, and child on earth—the possibility of sudden death as the result of a nuclear explosion. Perhaps just as fearful is the dehumanization of people living under nuclear threat. And so, to the inhabitants of what is truly the age of science, the products of technology are literally a matter of life and death. Modern man is deeply troubled because what *is* and what *could be* are so different. Listen to this National Association of Manufacturers "poet," no doubt bemused by the stunning symmetries of science:

"For the expanding, dynamic economy of America, the sky is indeed the limit. Now more than ever we must have confidence in America's capacity to grow. Guided by electronics, powered by atomic energy, geared to the smooth, effortless workings of automation, the magic carpet of our free economy heads for distant and undreamed horizons. Just going along for the ride will be the biggest thrill on earth!"[4]

In contrast William Samson Beck, American biochemist, maintains that to the mid-twentieth-century citizen, science is almost grotesquely ambivalent. He defines science thus:

"It is highly systematic in its approach to the real world, yet it is never complete and never reaches final conclusions.

"It is a model of certainty in its methodology and logic, yet its driving force is deliberate doubt and its results are probable, never certain.

74

"Though it may be local in origin, its conclusions are universal.

"It is the healer and builder and at the same time the propagator of untold suffering and death.

"Is it any wonder that science, the strong, the promising, the unforeseeable, the anarchical force in the modern world, should be the cause of acute anxiety?"[5]

Notice that Beck characterizes science as anarchical. I believe he means that free inquiry is, and should be, ungoverned; but it is this anarchical quality of science that causes anxiety. Our technology now produces an abundance of products and conditions which continually call for new human adaptation. Agriculture developed ten thousand years ago; the wheel was invented five thousand years ago; the steam engine, one hundred years ago; the airplane, sixty years ago; atomic energy was utilized just twenty years ago; and voyaging in space began in 1957. Notice the glacial progression of technological breakthroughs in earlier years as compared with today's floodtide.

Reflecting on the best standards of life and dignity, on the wide margin between an average educated man's abilities and his needs in this country, on the growing gross national product, on the good health and the affluence of the majority, it would be foolish to say that a drought would be preferable to a flood. But it is still more foolish to ignore the serious problems which have accompanied advances in science and technology.

Out of good health and affluence has come an epochal population increase. About 75 percent of all the people in the United States have been drawn into two hundred densely packed cities occupying only about 10 percent of our land—some 35,000 square miles. People at work, at play, and in the way they live, create environments that seriously threaten the well-being of the nation. American geochemist Harrison Brown has warned: "Man's survival now depends on how rapidly he accumulates knowledge concerning both his environment and himself and how effectively he learns to use that knowledge."[6]

Many Americans may nod wisely when confronted with such a warning, and yet the nation's love affair with the automobile continues, creating ever more air pollution and transforming green countryside and sections of great cities into ribbons of lifeless concrete. Mass transit systems remain inadequate. An atmosphere of dehumanizing materialism prevails, and the idealism and optimism that motivated our forefathers have been supplanted by disaffection among our young people who, in increasing numbers, seek escape in drugs. The atmosphere in many American cities is explosive, and over all hovers the ubiquitous threat of nuclear destruction.

These conditions are cited as concomitants of this day of science and technology. Those who would lay the causes of these enormous problems at the door of science display a lack of insight. Such problems in fact represent society's collective weaknesses magnified by technology. Far from exerting a malevolent influence, science, I believe, can serve as an agent of salvation. But American society must first determine where it wants to go and then must manage science and technology so that they will take us there.

76   I think that it is clear that twentieth-century man must

somehow relinquish the nineteenth-century obsession with the perfectibility of man, and of the related idea that novelty represents progress. The notion that every new technique or product represents an upward spiral of advancement is a delusion. The key word is control—of ourselves and of technology.

It is said that while the man of action must believe and the inquirer must doubt, the scientific investigator must do both. He is trained in the discipline formulated by Galileo Galilei (1564-1642), the Italian astronomer, mathematician, and physicist, a discipline requiring that the findings of one competent observer must be verified by another and yet another, until a hypothesis is arrived at. This is the way of science. One cannot say, the world is like this or like that. One can only suggest that our experience up to the present time is best represented by *this* kind of world.

I know of no better path to follow than that of the scientific method in finding the way out of present social crises. The way of science can be used to put down the anarchy of technology.

The joint effort of teams of social scientists has been used in the past to overcome grave danger. In World War II, the British marshaled their professors, and it has been said that they, and not the generals, saved the British Isles. They saved their country by applying the scientific method to every phase of warfare: zoologists, geneticists, mathematicians, psychologists, anthropologists, physicists, and chemists worked together in teams to solve problems presented by German bombers and submarines. Similarly, teams of social engineers can attack the dynamics of peace-time problems.

In 1700, when science began its shaking of the foundations, and the new scientific enlightenment swept the Western world, men challenged what they had been told was good, true, and beautiful and began to formulate their own ideas. Today some young men and women give vent to their feelings by waving placards, invading school buildings, and spurning reason. They are rejecting the old ideas, but are they formulating new ideas? Riots and ill-tempered and violent dissent are destructive; they produce no alternatives. Beneficial change, our history shows, is brought about by finding better ways, by thinking in new categories, by moving from hunch to proof. I hope that those people of all ages who reject what they see in today's society will also learn to examine reality dispassionately—the reality of the suffocating urban life, the reality of the nuclear nightmare, the reality of an undirected technology. Science can show them the way to change these realities. It can draw them into the joyful world of the spontaneous, the creative, and the ordered—all of the best that is waiting to be released by the inner resources of the mind.

The Paradox
of
Progress

JOHN H. GIBBONS

If, as Dr. Gibbons suggests, our society seems able to respond only in the face of crisis—and crisis of our own making, at that—we must examine what has gone into the making of both the clamoring "loud" crisis and the insidious "silent" crisis. The mixed blessings of an age of "progress" now must be recognized for what they are, in order to establish national priorities in the way technology is used.

The recent surge of interest in science and science education had its real roots much earlier in time. Science and technology have been growing exponentially for generations. Their impact on society began to be felt broadly with the industrial revolution and has sharply increased in the period since 1940. Their immense success in producing tangible benefits—goods and hardware for easier living and for more effective military defense—has caused the whole output of scientists and technologists to be regarded as a sacred cow. Rewards were piled at the doors of its producers, and budget proposals for research were approved nearly as blindly as were those for military expenditures. With Russia's first Sputnik in 1957, American interest in "science," and especially in science education, reached an even higher peak.

Many wonderful things have happened as a consequence of this neo-renaissance, but the blessings have been mixed, as Americans are beginning to realize. Along with its contributions to a better life, technology, as it has been known for decades, also proliferates awesome military weapons. But this fact hardly touches the daily lives of most people and unfortunately has become a sort of accepted payment in return for promises of "security" from the military. (In fact, many people have even come to view the thermonuclear weapon as a great peacemaker which literally forces nations to use alternatives to major war in political bargaining.) The new concern about science arises, I believe, from the realization that even the social benefits of technology have not been unqualified blessings. Consider some examples.

Over the past thirty years enormous strides have been made in developing means of lowering the incidence of disease and death. For example, collaborative work between biologists and engineers at the Oak Ridge National Laboratory, sponsored by the Atomic Energy Commission and the National Institutes of Health, has recently produced a technique called zonal ultracentrifugation that enables the separation of viruses into very nearly pure form. Using this technique, it has become possible to separate killed flu virus from the albumin and other ingredients of the culture in which it is grown. This centrifuged vaccine produces such markedly lower reactions that it can be safely administered to both the very young and the elderly. This is but one of many examples of the steady inroads being made on disease. While death rates continue their steady, historic decline in the industrialized world, they are plummeting in the so-called developing world, thanks to the relatively sudden injection of medical science and public health techniques from industrialized nations.

This lowering of death rates can rightly be heralded as a triumph of man over his environment, but it is producing new problems. First, the nature of the genetic pool is being changed by medical and social procedures which enable individuals with serious genetic deficiencies to reach sexual maturity and to procreate. Second, the sudden large imbalance between death rates and birth rates, especially

82

in the developing nations, is causing economic havoc and serious political unrest. Over half the world's people are undernourished or worse, and the continuing worldwide health campaign to lower death rates is in large measure responsible for this situation. Adlai Stevenson said in one of his last speeches that four slices of bread mean more to a hungry man than the four freedoms. When people are chronically underfed they are easy targets for the appeal of Communism or other totalitarian governments.

The United States, by making its now-vanished surplus foods available during drought years, has caused the people of India to become dependent upon marginal lands as steady food sources for their burgeoning population. Thus every agricultural year that is not an unusually good year means famine for India. New plant stocks and fertilizers are beginning to offset this trend, but offer only a short-term respite. The lowered death rates of the equatorial nations have increased their population explosion to the point that serious, chronic malnutrition (kwashiorkor) has attacked thousands of children during early life, often causing permanent brain damage and placing an additional strain on countries that are already strained to the limit in trying to provide the bare necessities of life.

The same humanitarian drive that undergirded the American commitment to lower death rates provides the current incentives to help provide for new food sources. Food yields have been increased by the development and introduction of new genetic material, pesticides, herbicides, and fertilizers, and techniques for water production, irrigation, and cultivation. Food yields are increasing, but these gains are not being made without cost. Ironically, the higher food yields are decreasing earlier incentives for family limitation, especially among more primitive people, and are increasing birth rates because they increase fertility. Furthermore, fertilizers, pesticides, and herbicides are finding their way into streams and are causing serious water quality problems. The automation of farming means loss of farm labor jobs and, consequently, hastens urbanization with its manifold problems.

Heroic, unconventional efforts will be required to combat food shortages over the next several decades. Studies at Oak Ridge have shown that broad extensions of agriculture are basically problems of energy. To produce the immense amount of energy required for massive increases in food production, "energy centers" are being designed which use giant nuclear reactors on fertile coastal deserts to supply the heat to heat and pump the water, run the equipment, and make fertilizer—literal food factories. It is not yet known what side effects these centers may have on the society of man, but they will certainly tend to revolutionize the social traditions of the food-hungry nations associated with this new technology.

The new affluence of the industrialized world has not been without its share of bad side effects. Pollution is a sign of what I would term "primitive affluence." American society must be placed largely in this class—where quality of environment always seems to be less important than monetary cost, where little economic consideration is given to aesthetic values. In my own state, Tennessee, Chattanooga, a mighty industrial city, has been for years the worst city in all of America in terms of particulate

84

matter in its air. Wealthy Nashville, gleaming bright with urban renewal and university expansion, still ingloriously dumps sufficient raw sewage and waste into the Cumberland River to be fined by the state for fish kills. A penalty for degradation should have been levied long ago. Tennessee has barely begun to enact legislation to control denuding of mountains by strip mines or to protect for recreational use some of its few remaining free-flowing streams. These streams are threatened by public organizations that all too often build dams to justify their own existence or to collect political spoils.

Throughout the nation, massive expressways have been built in and around cities with almost no forethought to their many ramifications. Only later is it discovered that these projects had in their very conception the seeds of economic destruction for the inner city and of aesthetic disaster for the land near the city. Currently, the development of a supersonic passenger jet is heavily subsidized. This jet will be economically feasible only if flights are allowed across the country. Millions of people will be condemned to daily sonic booms in order for comparatively few people to spend a little less time in the air. As an alternative, it has been seriously proposed that these planes be routed over less populous areas—over national parks, for example, where even now one can barely escape the noise and smell of the automobile. Meanwhile, public funds to attack the urgent problems of urban transportation and pollution from gasoline-driven cars (the source of over 50 percent of our air pollution) remain somehow unavailable.

85   All of these points have the common themes of: (1)

the too-rapid growth in population in most parts of the world, including the United States; and (2) no well-developed national policy of priorities in science and technology. Hence the "social" problems, collectively referred to as the Social Crisis, are intimately connected with the way we have used science and technology. We are in the midst of a number of social crises, probably more now than ever before in man's history, simply because of the record rapidity of change. It is convenient to divide the "crisis" into two components.

The first is the loud crisis; this encompasses such problems as living conditions in the urban ghetto or student unrest on the university campus. The most effective approach to this crisis has been to create sufficient stir to attract attention which is followed by political action. This technique fully deserves the title "crisis politics," and it *works,* reflecting the discouraging fact that in the United States society seems able to respond only in the face of a noisy crisis. Unquestionably the scientist and technologist, particularly the latter, have a very important supportive role to play in this area in the development of relevant hardware such as ways to build new cities that are truly livable.

The second is the silent crisis; in this category belong such problems as the rapid loss in quality of human life in most of the world, long-range changes in the environment caused by misuse of natural resources, and man's own image of himself and of society. It is to this crisis that the scientist and humanist bear an especially heavy responsibility. The goal of science education must be to instill in

86

every citizen an awareness of this silent crisis and further, to instill a sense of balance so that he does not permit his deep involvement in the more clamorous crisis to obscure the equally pressing need to resolve the more fundamental, silent crisis.

I certainly do not want to decry the basic activities and drives toward better health and "the good life." But I do feel that American society is continuing to operate from poor premises. We seem to have an addiction to the concept of growth as a fundamental measure of progress. Many times growth only masquerades as progress. Even now, in the face of wide recognition that excessive family size keeps many poor families locked in the cycle of poverty, government planners are proposing a guaranteed minimum family income that is proportional to family size —a sure incentive for the very poor to have more children.

National vision in the United States seems to suffer constantly from acute myopia. Long-range planning is well-nigh impossible in a subsistence society but should be of great concern in an affluent one. During public hearings in Gatlinburg, Tennessee, concerned with wilderness classification for parts of the Great Smoky Mountains National Park (June 13, 1966), the most distant future date alluded to by the political representatives was less than ten years away! Conservationists, scientists, and concerned citizens managed to put in a few words for the next generations, but by the time they were allowed to speak, most of the politicians had left the hearings.

Many important national decisions, especially those related to science and technology, seem to be made on the basis of what is *possible,* rather than what is *desirable,* for society. This reflects a tendency to regard technology as an irresistible force rather than as a servant and tool to be used to effect meaningful social progress. Isn't it time to challenge the statement, "You can't stop progress"?

It is time to rearrange national priorities. It is essential that our citizenry comprehend both the promises and limitations of science and technology, and it is the arena of education that provides the great opportunities for disseminating such knowledge. Now, more than ever before, universal and effective science teaching is necessary as a fundamental preparation for citizenship. The citizen today is more and more engulfed by the manifestations of science and technology—in his environment and in the sociological and political decisions he must make.

For too many citizens, science and technology have become accepted as a dominant force, but one which seems to defy appreciation or understanding by the average voter. The alarming rise of scientism in America is probably a manifestation of this attitude. Such an attitude bodes disaster for a Jeffersonian democracy in which the citizen participates knowledgeably and rationally in decision making. Science teachers must give their students an appreciation of scientific principles which is sufficiently sound to prevent future citizens from leaving science-related policy making to the elite.

Science education must be improved as a basis for disseminating job skills in an increasingly technological society. It is well known that poor education in elementary school, especially in mathematics, can haunt even a very bright student in later years. Society must recognize the immensity of the impact of the elementary-school years on the student's outlook, orientation, and motivation. Education must meet the challenge to create in the classroom an awareness of the interrelationships between things, between people, between disciplines—for example, the interplay between social problems and technology. Many of man's greatest challenges belong to those broadly educated in both natural science and social or political science.

Never before has man been so dependent upon science and technology for his comfort and livelihood. Because of technology, more people enjoy more abundant material life than was imaginable a century ago. It has become apparent, however, that technology is not a purely benevolent instrumentality. It is also the agent of environmental degradation. However, man can, if he wishes, employ technology as a tool to release him from his primitive affluence. But first he must give up his inflated image of himself as lord and master of this planet and learn to view himself instead as its custodian and caretaker.

The
Now Generation,
Science Teaching,
and
The Future

PHILIP C. RITTERBUSH

How can the message of these writers, and of concerned scientists and citizens everywhere, be translated into effective channels of communication? Society has looked too long to the past and present, relying on outdated modes of expression and reaction, letting the future take care of itself. In this final article, Dr. Ritterbush focuses on the future, and on future citizens. What to say to them, and how to say it, presents an exciting challenge. The message can be as mind-expanding, as awe-inspiring, as the very nature of the scientific endeavor. The future is upon us, and science can, indeed, meet it with hope.

In this year when the first men have landed on the moon, amidst a pageant of human events ever more rapidly unfolding, it is poignant that for so many the future has lost its appeal. We shrink from such prospects as overpopulation, the unraveling of the social fabric, the bruising impact of technology, and the loss of amenity. Indeed it seems that the future has been clouding over steadily since the bright dawn of hope for perpetual progress seen by the philosophers of the Era of Enlightenment two centuries ago. In a major study of men's attitudes toward the future as shown by religious beliefs and utopian writing, the Dutch sociologist Frederik Polak describes a very general trend toward doubt about man's prospects of progress. In his book, *The Image of the Future,* he shows how the anti-utopias, *1984* and *Brave New World*, are representative of a darkened image of the future which shadows the contemporary outlook.[1]

Paradoxically, the principal reason for this change in man's image of the future is the increased pace of social and technological change which has brought the future closer and made it seem directly accessible. It used to be that the destiny to which men entrusted their dreams was so remote and unrealizable that they usually applied themselves to workaday concerns, thinking the world of the future too far off for them ever to enter. To most it was enough to be working toward a better world for their children or succeeding generations. But the conquests of

93

SCIENCE LOOKS AT ITSELF

energy and of distance have compressed intervals of change, altering the experience and seeming velocity of time itself. All at once the future is here. Today's children are already its denizens. Their perception of this key fact accounts for much that seems unsettling in their cultural responses.

American anthropologist Margaret Mead stated the matter very well in one of her "Man and Nature" lectures:

"For now, nowhere in the whole world are there any elders who know what the children know, no matter how remote and simple the societies in which the children live. In the past there were always some elders who knew more —in terms of experience, of having grown up within a system—than any children. Today there are none. It is not only that parents are no longer a guide, but that there are no guides, in the older sense of the term, whether one seeks them in one's own country, or in China, or in India. There are no elders who know what those who have been reared in the last 20 years know about what the next 20 years will be."[2]

It is because America has arrived in the future that the Negro will no longer wait for another generation to accomplish social changes that are within the nation's capacity in the here and now. Nor do today's students heed requests to wait patiently for yet another generation while their elders tinker with the machinery of higher education or make minor fine tuning adjustments in social priorities. This is the now generation, quite simply, because the future is right now, and many hopes can no longer be postponed.

I think it is correct to say that in recent years America's course has been tending in directions which darkened the future, so that it has been all too easy to lose heart. But for today's students that remote and sadly dwindling future has become a present charged with possibilities for their participation and involvement. The promise of the future has been reborn in today's youth. The teacher, custodian of the past and outfitter for the future of each year's advancing rank of students, is a point of junction between the present as it reflects our accomplishments and the future as it is experienced by students. And of no sector of teaching can this be more true than for science teaching. What portrayal of the future of elementary and secondary education in science may be found to be worth transforming into a present?

The greatest challenge to science education arises from the democratization of education in recent years. Fifty years ago it was arguable that science teachers were engaged principally in providing precollege education to future scientists. Today they seek to acquaint the citizen of tomorrow with science as a prime force in the social universe. Claude Gatewood of The Educational Research Council of America has observed:

"In a society that is as scientifically and technologically oriented as ours is today, all students should be broadly educated in science, in its processes, its products, its philosophy, and its impact on society. . . . The single most important goal of school science must be to prepare scientifically literate citizens for the future."[3] The goal of preparing future scientists he considers to be merely "secondary."

95   The broadening of the democratic vista requires that

education confront the jarring challenges of the youth culture, with its flight from rationality and indulgence in sensations of light and color. The disturbing images of poster art and psychedelic saturation of the senses may strike some as inimical to the life of the mind. But I do not believe this is in fact so. There is much in the career of science to uphold the view that the sense of sight and mediating images play a primary role in the creative process. Repeatedly transcending the merely verbal, science has drawn special insights from similarities or differences which are *perceived* before they are fully understood. The stage of verbalization comes only after one has his results and is preparing to write them up. One reason for the primacy of vision in science is the role of explanatory models. The construct for reality is nearly always visual in some important way and sometimes exclusively so. At times the scientist fixes his entire attention upon the model. He manipulates it as he might a puzzle, or he rotates it through a succession of carefully chosen different circumstances, looking for invariance or decisive change. The application of mathematics to physical systems frequently depends upon the subtle play of symmetry concepts: reflections and rotations performed in visualized space. American biologist James D. Watson wrote in *The Double Helix* that he looked wonderingly at spiral staircases on a weekend visit to Oxford while trying to work out the structure of RNA and thereafter made a special study of spiral structure wherever he could find it in nature. And then, touching on a higher mystery, when he determined the helical structure of DNA, he observed that it was too pretty not to be true.[4]

96

Science educators are faced by a major transformation of preferred modes of knowing among high school and college-age youngsters. They emphasize the visual over the verbal, the responsive over the cognitive, the affective over the rational. But I do not believe this excludes science from their consideration. The kinetic light-shows so popular with today's youngsters seem like nothing so much as an imaginary experience of a complex atomic model as it might be seen from the nucleus. I hold, moreover, that students are fascinated by all aspects of the experience of reality, including the most profound philosophical problems. And then there is the unusual role of illustration in biology—as the famous German botanist Julius von Sachs (1832-1897) observed: What has not been drawn has not been seen. How often a problem is turned out into the subconscious for a kind of visual reintegration. No, I do not view the visual appetites of modern youth as a threat to science. Their pursuit of challenging visual experiences may indicate a culturally mediated rapport with science, an intuitive grasp of its processes and nature. So much of science is nonverbal, visual, and experienced as pattern rather than precise image, that I am prepared to argue that most of the loose and seemingly irrational elements in today's youth scene may be regarded instead as a direct contribution from science—creating new opportunities for the talented science teacher.

Consider Gatewood's assertion that our primary aim in the schools is enlightenment for the citizen rather than training of the future scientist. As it applies to environmental education I have served as a staff assistant in the

United States Senate and briefly in the White House, where I have been faced directly by citizen responses to a number of environmental problems. It has been my experience that a successful resolution of problems of environmental management always requires the citizen to have a reasonable appreciation of the scientific factors involved. I am thinking particularly of the limited test ban treaty in 1963, but there were, and still are, many other instances. The kinds of problems posed by interaction between society and the physical environment are seldom clear-cut. Rarely, if ever, is there a simple "scientific" answer unanimously agreed upon by experts. Rather, there is usually an interaction of competing interests, conjecturing uncertainly about the long-range future consequences of actions despite an imperfect understanding of even their present consequences. Proper responses depend directly upon the extent of public understanding.

I would caution emphatically that scientists do not always act to foster disinterested understanding. The dust bowl of the 1930s eventuated from a failure to appreciate the finding of American naturalist John Wesley Powell (1834–1902) that the eastern slope of the Rockies and the high plains could not support intensive cultivation. There was a contrary idea in the 1880s and 1890s, defended by many scientists, that rain would follow the plow —whatever was furrowed would be better watered. It was a ridiculous idea, but it was very influential. Railroads were then greedily arranging for land sales in the Rocky Mountain West and eagerly publicized this spurious scientific justification for a land rush.

98

The rape of the environment continues relentlessly. As often as not there is a trumped-up scientific justification. Man persists in the delusion that environmental mastery consists in gigantic engineering works. Again and again one hears of grandiose projects that have gone astray, such as irrigation schemes in Pakistan which have caused the accumulation of surface salts which impair the quality of agricultural land and harmfully alter the water table in some areas. Yet plans become ever more ambitious and now include the regulation of weather on a global scale and colossal interference with major climatic regimes, as with the notion of turning the Amazon Basin into an inland sea. The spurious scientific justifications for these projects are frequently fed by the program interests of a government agency hell-bent on implementing a one-sided solution reflecting its official diagnosis of a situation.

One more bit of history worth recounting in this context is the way the U.S. Forest Service propagandized on behalf of a larger staff and more millions to fight fires. In the 1920s a pioneer ecologist at Yale named H. H. Chapman was coming to understand that periodic burning was necessary to preserve the purity of stands of long-leaf pine in the southeastern states and that seedlings of this species could withstand fire after they reached a certain age. Observers from abroad had noticed that the Indians had periodically burned those pine stands, employing what was becoming a well-accepted forestry practice elsewhere in the world, as in British management of stands of chir pine in the Himalayas. The U.S. Forest Service, intent on its national fire-suppression program, would not sanction such heresy. Its own professional employees advocating periodic burning in long-leaf pine were refused the right to publish papers supporting Chapman's position, and ill-designed experiments were cooked up in an effort to bolster the official view, while millions of pieces of promotional literature flooded schools throughout the Southeast and numerous "educational" films were thoughtfully supplied to teachers. The climax of the Forest Service publicity campaign was the elevation of Smokey the Bear to the status of a national hero. He has now gained that highest of accolades, a place in the Smithsonian Institution, prominently displayed in the National Zoological Park along with a cluster of posters provided by the Forest Service.

I have fought fires and been appalled by their devastation. What I am advocating is not an end of protection but a more balanced understanding of natural systems. If it had not been for periodic fires maintaining the savannah of eastern Africa a million and a half years ago, man's prehuman ancestors might never have come down from the trees! And fire plays a role in sustaining many desirable forest conditions today.

I mention historical examples because the public is too often told that environmental science is a new discipline which offers comprehensive new solutions if only they are taught widely enough. Environmentally oriented science, often under government aegis, has instead been for generations a primary contributor to the abuse of the environment. The surest safeguard is a citizenry with strong defenses against the plagues of publicism and with a sound understanding of the intricate web of ecological circumstances in which they are involved. The ecologic crisis is the surest evidence that science education can no longer be limited to the few who will have scientific careers. Unless the education of the many who must govern is accomplished, it will be impossible to maintain the quality of the environment. Therefore, the introduction of vastly more effective environmental education becomes a priority aim of science teaching in the future.[5]

It can reliably be predicted that the next twenty-five years will modify radically present-day understanding of environmental influences and the limits of human adaptability. Members of the public will have to appraise new mechanisms, new concepts, and sweeping revisions of common-sense views. It is not enough to peddle slogans or tolerate the official view that environmental conditions are only just about as bad as they ought to become. Students must be given an understanding of primary environmental processes in order to become acquainted with the delicacy of the relationship between organisms and their environments and the limits of tolerance the conservative character of genetic mechanisms impose upon living systems.

Because of the depth and universality of understanding which will be required in the field of environmental biology, educators should be mindful of better ways to use visual learning processes. One domain of study which I think may be developed especially fruitfully is oceanography— not in a gee-whiz, breathless-triumph-of-discovery manner, but rather through the exposition of delicate living systems, exploiting their inherent fascination and visual appeal. I frequently attend pious conclaves on the devotion of science to man's progress, and the presses have been pouring out unreadable books on the subject. But to sense something of what could be done to foster a wider understanding of man's environmental relationships through teaching marine science, read Eleanor Clark's lovely and poetic book, *The Oysters of Locmariaquer*, which describes the cultivation of oysters on the Atlantic coast of France.[6] The book gives ample descriptions of the life cycle of the oyster and its entire environmental regime as they have contributed to man's successes and failures in his centuries-long effort to master techniques of cultivation—all told in the most glorious limpid prose, with remarkable sympathy for the people of Brittany and their everyday lives.

This book is worth a dozen pompous products of the textbook industry. Moreover, it constitutes an implied rebuke to all environmental educators in that it beats them so thoroughly at their own game. There are similar stories to be found in the decline of the Atlantic salmon, for example; or in the end of the whaling industry, first in the Bay of Biscay three centuries ago, then in the eastern Arctic one century ago, and now in the Antarctic—stories which are meaningful, relevant, laden with scientific and human interest.

Another theme in the future development of science teaching will be greater attention to science as process. Here science teachers will be building on the solid accomplishments of the last generation in broadening subject-matter coverage, especially in high-school-level science courses. But it is necessary to go even further.

102

One of the least satisfactory aspects of contemporary science education is the contrived experiment, whether a rote laboratory exercise or one of the more fashionable experiments in a modern discovery learning sequence. A student may indeed learn through discovery, and ever more significant contributions may be expected from *strategies* which allow the student to recreate patterns of knowledge as he encounters them during free exploration. But I believe that an important criticism may fairly be made of too much reliance on discovery learning, and it is the same criticism which may be entered against the cookbook laboratory manual: The most important creative process in science is the design of experiments or courses of observation derived from the analysis of existing knowledge. The student cannot understand how science works without an insight into the ceaseless critical process which finds gaps in knowledge and devises means to repair them. Otherwise it is too easy for him to conceive of science as nothing more than a collection of facts. Science is not, after all, a way of "getting at" the facts but a system of inquiry within which facts take on meaning. Throughout the student's life, science will disclose new relationships and forge new concepts. It is a sign of failure for any student ever to conclude that he knows enough about science.

It is my hope that every high-school science course would devote a week or more to detailed consideration of one classic experiment or controversy in its subject. Such a study would portray the intellectual conditions which prevail before a decisive advance, the existence of shortcomings of concepts or data, uncertainties about the most profitable course to pursue, the role which luck occasionally plays, and the need for imagination and the other qualities which make for success. It could also lead the student to understand science as a series of responses to the unexplained rather than the sum total of what happens to be known at any moment.

Part of the task of portraying the process of science should be to familiarize students with the everyday appearance of science—here again a significant opportunity for visual learning. Let the laboratory, the field station, the satellite platform, the refinery become as familiar to the student as the bank or office building. The environments of research are usually developed in response to what scientists and engineers want. They bespeak the nature of the creative enterprise and tell us a great deal without any need for words. And they serve to emphasize something else very important about science—that it is a varied enterprise, not the exclusive preserve of geniuses or, for that matter, of freaks. I suspect we are not yet at that point where high school students may choose a career in science without being thought peculiar by some of their friends. Those subtle tyrannies by which a student becomes imprisoned in the limited meshes of what his friends understand or value may be countered very effectively by illustrating the life of science. It is ordinary and human, and yet also it underscores a point made earlier—the future has arrived. We are in it. The visual evidence, from the surface of the moon or the computer center, is overwhelming. Buck Rogers, once scorned as unreal, is now obsolete.

Another theme likely to become dominant in the future

of science teaching is the introduction to the classroom of

the sciences of man. At the Smithsonian Institution we have been experimenting with *Man: A Course of Study*, an upper-elementary project produced by Peter Dow for the Education Development Center, Inc., of Cambridge, Massachusetts.

One of the most appealing aspects of this course for our Institution, which is devoted to open visual education in museums, is the primary emphasis on media. Booklets, records, filmstrips, maps, posters, photomurals, educational games, and independent project materials are designed to complement the sixteen films which are the core of the curriculum. The concepts presented in the course, and most of the course materials, are based on recent work on the research front: the Austrian zoologist and psychologist Konrad Lorenz and Nikolaas Tinbergen, the Dutch zoologist, on behavior patterns in birds; American anthropologists Sherwood Washburn and Irven DeVore on group structure and behavior in baboons, the only ground-adapted primate other than man; and Danish explorer Knud Rasmussen (1879–1933), and the ethnofilms of Turkish anthropologist Asen Balikci on the Netsilik Eskimos. Here students encounter fresh and challenging experiences from which they can draw a set of workable models for analyzing the nature of the social world in which they live. They gain insights into a rapidly developing and highly significant province of science.

Man: A Course of Study has been tested with several thousand students so far and has proved an effective demonstration that elusive, difficult concepts about social processes may be convincingly presented through the use of media in support of sound, science-based concepts.

This course of study is based on existing work on animal behavior. Other courses, based on research in various fields, are also possible. The three-layer cake of biology-chemistry-physics will, I believe, be set aside in favor of interdisciplinary approaches combining the natural and social sciences in a flexible array of fresh instructional opportunities.

Such discerning contemporary biologists as Marshall Nirenberg of the United States and Jacques Monod of France have stated their desire to abandon their earlier specialties in order to work on the staggering complexities of the brain—an organ and neurophysiological focus that is bound to attract some of the very greatest minds of this age to analysis and discovery. The brain is at least an order of magnitude more complex than the genetic processes which have so dominated biological thinking in recent years. A generation of lavish discovery unquestionably awaits those who are willing to seek to elucidate our mental life. I suspect that the present categories of madness and sanity will undergo change, as the French cultural historian Michel Foucault has so strongly suggested. The oft-heralded problems of the city, involving stress, crime, anomie, and social breakdowns will increasingly attract purposeful investigators, and society can anticipate major accomplishments in applied social science in years to come. As the research fronts of the scientific enterprise are redrawn, I am convinced that science teaching will adapt to the changing configuration of knowledge. And again visual learning will play a privileged role.

The theme I deem most important I have left until last, and that is the need to treat science in terms of the whole culture of which it is a part. Science has truly never been a distinct province of human thought, secure and self-sufficient. Instead it is part of a larger culture, to which it contributes and from which it draws much of its strength. So it becomes of the highest importance to relate science teaching to the humanities and the arts. Here the scientifically gifted student may find a sure approach to more general human concerns, while for the student less skilled in scientific procedures, the humanities may provide a superior means of introducing the world of science.

It is futile to strive to insulate science from questions of social purpose. Decisions about the areas of science to receive greatest emphasis in the next quarter century will be public ones in many ways. First, the establishment of large programs which result in support for different fields of science necessarily involves government and public: witness the space program or nuclear science. Second, our ability to develop certain fields depends upon the extent to which students elect to pursue them, which in turn will reflect prevailing social assessments of their importance and appeal. The decision as to which human purposes shall be given greatest priority in extending the scientific research effort cannot be made by a philosopher king somewhere in Washington—it must be a composite of many decisions, dreams, discoveries, and desires. The role of the science teacher in this process is a very considerable one, leading some students to see that science may be a means to their desired end of human improvement or social betterment, and, it is to be hoped, giving almost all students a sense of the place of science in society.

107 Society may be witnessing the portents of a student re-

action against science. Science is too often regarded as a troublesome factor in military power or as a mechanical process inimical to man's sense of his own humanity. I believe that there is a danger of representing science as cold, analytic, passionless, dehumanized, and unfeeling. Again, the visual presentation of the materials and images of science should dispel this unfortunate error. The creations of science are as beautiful as those of the arts (if not necessarily in the same way); they draw upon the same human wellsprings of feeling and desire. In fact there is frequently an uncanny resemblance between the scientist's image of reality and the artist's projection of his feelings.

About ten years ago I began to experience before certain works of modern art a strong suspicion that they manifested an essential affinity with biological concepts of form. In the paintings of Paul Klee and Max Ernst I thought I recognized certain generalized principles of form which I had known from microscopy and anatomy. The sculpture of Hans Arp seemed to reveal curves of growth like those which had so fascinated Goethe and other poets who greatly admired the shapes of growing things. Amid the swirling shapes of Kandinsky, Miró, and Gorky I thought I detected vestigial outlines of protozoa, plankton, and growing tissues. Yet these were abstract works lacking any apparent reference to reality. Was it possible that they reflected some kind of rapport with scientific discoveries of form, the new landscape of microscopic phenomena delineated over the past century by the German naturalist Christian Ehrenberg (1795–1876), the American anatomist Joseph Leidy (1866–1932), and so many others?

108   I recalled that many of the great microscopists of the

nineteenth century were exceedingly interested in art. Among the Germans, biologist Ernst Heinrich Haeckel (1834–1919) and geologist Theodor Boveri (1862–1915) were landscapists, and zoologist Carl Chun (1852–1914) decorated his house with frescoes. The French-born zoologist Franz Doflein (1873–1924) painted in water-color. Santiago Ramón y Cajal (1852–1934), the great Spanish neurophysicist and Nobel prizewinner, said that he owed many of his discoveries to the sense of beauty which led him to look for hidden relationships of size and structure.

Conversely the art critic Leo Steinberg has written: "Wittingly, or through unconscious exposure, the non-objective artist draws much of his iconography from the visual data of the scientist—from magnifications of minute natural textures, from telescopic vistas, submarine scenery, and X-ray photographs. . . . It is apparently in these gestating images, shapes antecedent to the visible, that many abstract painters recognize an intenser mode of natural truth."[7]

The visual content of much twentieth-century art is drawn from science, and the arts are powerful aids to the scientist's powers of perception and analysis.[8] I believe that science teaching in the future will increasingly involve the arts, just as the visual arts of the next twenty-five years will increasingly involve the sciences and technologies which are so expressive of our age and indicative of its highest capabilities. I venture to say that the aesthetic content of science offers the surest way to wider understanding of its conceptual content and character as process, by both students and the public at large. If today's students display an ardent interest in visual aspects of science, it may well be that they have penetrated close to its essence and made it part of themselves. The changing nature of student expectations offers to the future science teacher a bright opportunity to widen the curriculum, to do more justice to the delicate processes binding organisms to their environments, to create a wider understanding of what science itself is like to those who conduct research, and to include those aspects of science directly relevant to man. The realization of these opportunities will be an exacting and difficult task, but one that may make the next quarter century the most exciting in the history of science education, both in the schools and in the continuing education that must be a part of our adult lives.

REFERENCE NOTES

INDEX

REFERENCE NOTES

RAPPAPORT: PURPOSE, PROPERTY, AND
ENVIRONMENTAL DISASTER

1. Gregory Bateson, "Effects of Conscious Purpose on Human Adaptation" (unpublished paper prepared for Werner-Gren Symposium, 1968).
2. Roy A. Rappaport, *Pigs for the Ancestors* (New Haven, Conn.: Yale University Press, 1968).
3. John Kenneth Galbraith, *The New Industrial State* (Boston: Houghton Mifflin, 1967).

STODDARD: MUST ECONOMIC EXPANSION
DOOM THE ENVIRONMENT?

1. Arnold W. Reitze, "Wastes, Water and Wishful Thinking," *Case—Western Law Review* (November 1968), p. 382.
2. Joseph Wood Krutch (unpublished statement to Department of the Interior secretarial staff, May 1967).

SAUNDERS: THE RISKS OF DISBELIEF

1. Garrett Hardin, "The Tragedy of the Commons," *Science* (December 13, 1968), pp. 1243-1248.
2. Barry Commoner, *Science and Survival* (New York: The Viking Press, 1966).
3. Norbert Wiener, "Some Moral and Technical Consequences of Automation," *Science* (May 6, 1960), p. 1355.
4. Commoner, *op. cit.,* pp. 71-72; data from *Economic Viability after Thermonuclear War: The Limits of Feasible Production* (Santa Monica, California: Rand Corporation, 1963).
5. Commoner, *op. cit.,* p. 77.
6. President's Science Advisory Committee, *Restoring the Quality of Our Environment* (Washington, D. C.: Government Printing Office, November, 1965). Discussed in Commoner, *op. cit.,* p. 11.
7. Hardin, *loc. cit.,* p. 1244.

113

8. U Thant, *International Planned Parenthood News,* No. 168 (February, 1968), p. 3.

MC GEE: THE WAY OF SCIENCE

1. Stuart Chase, *The Most Probable World* (New York: Harper and Row, 1968), p. viii.
2. Quoted in *ibid.,* p. xiii.
3. James B. Conant, *Modern Science and Modern Man* (New York: Columbia University Press, 1952), p. 36.
4. National Association of Manufacturers, *Calling All Jobs* (New York: National Association of Manufacturers, October 1957), p. 21.
5. William S. Beck, *Modern Science and the Nature of Life* (New York: Harcourt, Brace and Co., 1957), p. 4.
6. Harrison Brown, "The Scientific Revolution—A Perspective," in Gerald W. Elbers and Paul Duncan (eds.), *The Scientific Revolution* (Washington: Public Affairs Press, 1959), p. 11.

RITTERBUSH: THE NOW GENERATION, SCIENCE TEACHING, AND THE FUTURE

1. Frederik Polak, *The Image of the Future* (Dobbs Ferry, N. Y.: Oceana Publications, Inc., 1967).
2. Margaret Mead, "Generation Gap," *Science* (April 11, 1969), p. 135.
3. Claude Gatewood, "The Science Curriculum Viewed Nationally," *The Science Teacher,* 35 (November, 1968), p. 20.
4. James Dewey Watson, *The Double Helix* (New York: Atheneum, 1968).
5. For citations to H. H. Chapman and other historical examples, see Philip C. Ritterbush, "Environment and Historical Paradox," *General Systems,* 13 (1969), pp. 107-114.
6. Eleanor Clark, *The Oysters of Locmariaquer* (New York: Vintage Books, 1967).
7. Leo Steinberg, "The Eye Is a Part of the Mind," *Partisan Review,* 20 (1953), p. 210.
8. Philip C. Ritterbush, *The Art of Organic Forms* (New York: Random House, Inc., 1968).

INDEX

About the Authors

ROY A. RAPPAPORT is associate professor of anthropology at The University of Michigan, Ann Arbor. As a cultural anthropologist, his main theoretical interest is in the relationship between religion and ecology. In addition to numerous articles, he has published a monograph, *Pigs for the Ancestors,* on the Maring people of the New Guinea Highlands and is co-author of *Archaeology of Mo'orea, French Polynesia.*

CHARLES H. STODDARD is a private resource consultant and also manages a 300-acre tree farm in Minong, Wisconsin. As a professional forester and resource manager, he has served with the U. S. Forest Service, the Bureau of Agricultural Economics, Resources for the Future, and as executive director of the Citizens Advisory Committee on Recreation and Natural Beauty. During the 1960s he headed Secretary of the Interior Udall's Resources Planning Staff and served as director of the Bureau of Land Management for three years. His published works include *Essentials of Forestry Practice* and *Land for the Future.*

JOHN H. HELLER is founder and president of The New England Institute, Ridgefield, Connecticut, an organization dedicated to interdisciplinary basic research. Long an exponent of breaking down the barriers between the various sciences, he has served on the faculty of the Yale University School of Medicine, as project director for the U. S. Atomic Energy Commission, and as a consultant to the Navy (on nuclear submarines), the Air Force (on manned satellites), and the National Academy of Sciences (on climatology and space exploration).

WALTER L. SAUNDERS is associate professor of science education at Utah State University, Logan. He has taught physics, chemistry, photography, and applied science at the secondary-school level and is currently consultant to the Weber Schools exemplary center for team teaching, an ESEA Title III project. Dr. Saunders is also science consultant for Educational Consulting Services, Utah State University, and is a member of various scientific and educational societies.

LEROY AUGENSTEIN (1928-1969) was professor and chairman of the department of biophysics, Michigan State University, East Lansing. He held positions as biophysicist with the Brookhaven National Laboratory and with the Atomic Energy Commission. In 1960-61, Dr. Augenstein was science coordinator for the U. S. science exhibit at the Seattle World's Fair. His publications have included works on enzyme structure and function, applications of information theory to biology, and information processing by humans. He is also the author of the recent book, *Come, Let Us Play God.*

GALE W. MCGEE, senior U. S. Senator from Wyoming, is chairman of the Senate Committee on Post Office and Civil Service and a member of the Senate Appropriations Committee and of various Foreign Relations subcommittees. His work on development of reclamation and water resource projects for the Rocky Mountain area led to his appointment to the Special Senate Committee on Water Resources. Prior to entering politics in 1958, Senator McGee taught speech and history in Nebraska high schools, at Nebraska Wesleyan University, Iowa State College, and the Universities of Chicago and Wyoming. He is a member of the Theodore Roosevelt Association and the Isaak Walton League, as well as numerous professional associations.

JOHN H. GIBBONS is a group leader, nuclear geophysics, in the physics division of the Oak Ridge National Laboratory, Oak Ridge, Tennessee, and director of the Laboratory's project for the study of environmental quality. He has also served as head of the university participation program of the Oak Ridge Institute of Nuclear Studies and was a participant in the national defense study group under E. P. Wigner. Dr. Gibbons is a member of the Sierra Club, the Wilderness Association, and various honorary scientific societies. He is an active proponent of planned parenthood and conservation of natural resources.

PHILIP C. RITTERBUSH is director of the Office of Academic Programs of the Smithsonian Institution, Washington, D. C. His special interest is in the place of science in modern culture, a subject on which he developed a graduate seminar at Yale University in 1962-63. He has worked on aspects of science and public policy under President Kennedy's science advisor, Jerome Wiesner; as a legislative assistant in the United States Senate; and as assistant to the secretary of the Smithsonian Institution for policy analysis and planning. He has also taught and lectured on these subjects at a number of universities. Dr. Ritterbush is associated with the Commission on the Year 2000 of the American Academy of Arts and Sciences. His published works include *Overtures to Biology,* which deals with the relationship between eighteenth-century natural science and literary ideas, and *The Art of Organic Forms.*